For Guy
AUGUST 2015

PAUL + Suzy

This is our first 'green' book - enjoy!

Many congrats on your wedding - so, so happy for you BOTH!!

Lots of love

Pie xxx
Clare xxx
Jack Cosby xxxxxxx

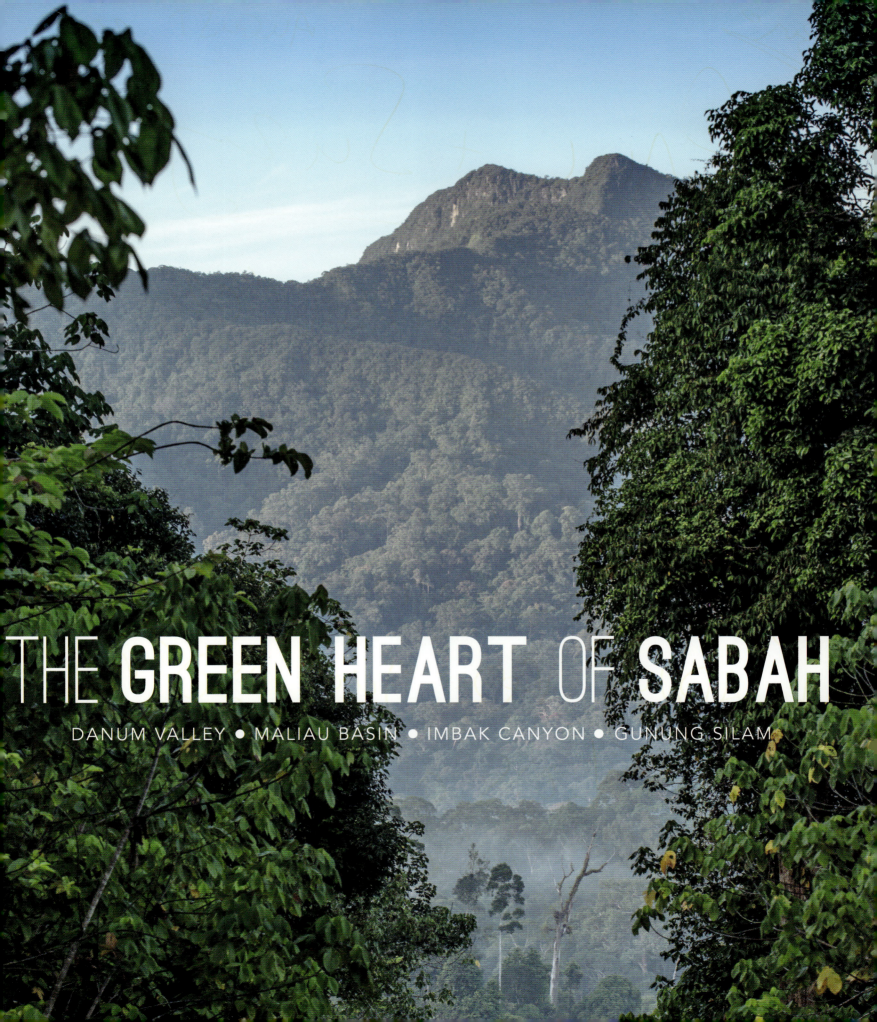

GREEN HEART OF SABAH

NUM VALLEY • MALIAU BASIN • IMBAK CANYON • GUNUNG SILAM

Author
Matt Oldfield

Photographers
Jason Isley, Ch'ien C. Lee, Christian Loader,
Matt Oldfield & Gilbert Woolley

scubazoo Publications

in association with Sabah Forestry

To Wendy Hutton:

Thank you for your guidance, inspiration and knowledge. 'The Green Heart of Sabah' would not have been created without your passion for Sabah and its forests.

MANAGING EDITOR	*Jason Isley*
PROJECT EDITOR	*Gilbert Woolley*
ASSISTANT EDITOR	*Christian Loader*
ART EDITOR	*Karen Chao*
TEXT	*Matt Oldfield*
ADDITIONAL TEXT	*Datuk Sam Mannan*
	Glen Reynolds
RESEARCHER	*Kristen Soong*
SCIENTIFIC CONSULTANT	*Ch'ien C. Lee*

Produced by Scubazoo Publications
2014 © Scubazoo Images Sdn. Bhd.
www.scubazoo.com
ISBN 978-967-10528-3-9

All rights reserved. No part of this publication may be reproduced, stored in a retrieval system, or transmitted in any form or by any means, electronic, mechanical, photo-copying, recording or otherwise, without the prior permission of the copyright owners.

The contents of this book are believed to be correct at the time of printing. Nevertheless, the publishers cannot be held responsible for any errors or omissions or for changes in the detail given in this book or for the consequences of any reliance on the information provided by the same. This does not affect your statutory rights.

Printed by KHL Printing Co Pte Ltd
57 Loyang Drive
Singapore 508968

MIX
Paper from responsible sources
FSC® C004791

Front cover:
Left: Rhinoceros Hornbill (*Buceros rhinoceros*), Imbak Canyon.
Middle: Maliau Falls, Maliau Basin.
Right: Bornean Orangutan (*Pongo pygmaeus morio*), Danum Valley.

Inside front cover: Close-up of a Bornean Angle-headed Lizard (*Gonocephalus borneensis*), Imbak Canyon.

Back cover: Wallace's Flying Frog (*Rhacophorus nigropalmatus*), Danum Valley.

Inside back cover: Close-up of Wallace's Flying Frog (*Rhacophorus nigropalmatus*), Danum Valley.

Page 1: Gunung Kuli, Imbak Canyon.

Page 2 & 3: Wallace's Flying Frog, (*Rhacophorous nigropalmatus*), Danum Valley.

Page 4 & 5: Crimson Marsh Glider (*Trithemis aurora*), Danum Valley.

Page 8: A herd of Bornean Pygmy Elephants (*Elephas maximus borneensis*) in Sungai Imbak, Imbak Canyon.

CONTENTS

Foreword

Introduction

Danum Valley Conservation Area

Maliau Basin Conservation Area

Imbak Canyon Conservation Area

Gunung Silam

Gallery - Green Heart's flora & fau

Forest management

Behind the lens

Acknowledgements

Photography credits

Sponsors

Index

MESSAGE FROM DATUK SERI PANGLIMA MUSA HAJI AMAN
The Right Honourable Chief Minister of Sabah

Sabah is blessed with some of the highest biodiversity on our planet and within the vast forests that form the 'Green Heart' of Sabah, a teeming variety of plants and animals can be found living together in highly complex ecosystems. These forests represent the last refuge for highly endangered species such as Clouded Leopards and Bornean Pygmy Elephants and provide forest-related services such as watershed protection, soil preservation and carbon sequestration. Our forests represent a significant fraction of Sabah's natural wealth – both in terms of their remarkable biodiversity and economic value.

The Sabah Forestry Department has long recognised the importance of proper forest management and since the late 1960s – when the Forest Enactment and Forest Rules came into force – has evolved to become a global leader in Sustainable Forest Management (SFM). In 1985, the department, Sabah Foundation and the Royal Society UK entered into a long-term partnership and established the Tropical Forest Research Programme at Danum Valley. Subsequently, Danum Valley has become a world-renowned research centre and ecotourism destination, providing scientists and tourists alike with access to one of the most important forest areas in the world. In 1989, Sabah introduced SFM techniques and research at the joint Malaysian-German Sustainable Forest Management Project at Deramakot Forest Reserve. In 1990, Reduced Impact Logging was introduced across the state. In 1992, the world's first forest carbon project was initiated at the INFRAPRO site at Ulu Segama Forest Reserve. In more recent years, we have continued to strive towards developing unique and sustainable management techniques, whilst progressive and forward-thinking implementation of legislation has led to the preservation of much of Sabah's forest land – in a region where the degradation and fragmentation of forests has become a significant threat to their viability.

FOREWORD

Today, nearly half of Sabah's landmass falls under the protection of the Sabah Forestry Department – approximately 3.9 million hectares – and 18 percent of Sabah is now totally protected. Sites such as Ulu Segama-Malua, Trusmadi, Danum Valley, Maliau Basin and Imbak Canyon have become synonymous with biodiversity conservation and sustainable resource use, and important ecotourism destinations for tourists wishing to experience Sabah's pristine rainforests. Science and research programmes continue, and the Sabah Forestry Department will be embarking on a number of ambitious projects and joint partnerships to further enhance the protection accorded to Sabah's forests. For example, the current Danum Valley, Maliau Basin, Ulu-Segama and Imbak Canyon conservation corridor is being expanded to include forest reserves such as Gunung Silam and additional mixed-use forest ares, with the view to developing management policy that focuses on biodiversity and forest services, whilst remaining financially self-sustaining through the use of conservation-compatible techniques. Such management strategies may well become an important model for SFM in other parts of the globe. In addition, Petronas has recently announced a joint venture with Sabah Foundation, Sabah Wildlife Department, Sabah Forestry Department and other organisations, and will be funding the further development of facilities at Imbak Canyon turning it into a world-class centre for research and science. The future of conservation and science in Sabah's forests is bright.

2014 marks the 100th year anniversary of the Sabah Forestry Department and what better way to celebrate this important milestone than with Scubazoo's stunning book. *The Green Heart of Sabah* is a glimpse into the remarkable forest world that has been of such value to the people of Sabah. Highlighting both the beautiful landscapes and bountiful diversity, the book will stand as a permanent reminder to us all of the importance of conservation and sustainable resource use.

Datuk Seri Panglima Musa Haji Aman
The Right Honourable Chief Minister of Sabah

INTRODUCTION

By Datuk Sam Mannan
Director of Forestry, Sabah

Within the 'Green Heart' of Sabah lies some of the most remarkable ecosystems on our planet. Dense, verdant forests stretch across rugged mountains and steep valleys whilst beautiful, crystal-clear rivers cut a path across the landscape, cascading down tiers of waterfalls on their way to the sea. Up above, along exposed ridges shrouded in mists and clouds, stunted forests blanketed in mosses shelter rare Pitcher Plants and unique plant communities, whilst below, in the still, humid air of the lowland forest, Clouded Leopards, Bornean Orangutans and Pygmy Elephants can still be found, living amongst the buttresses of towering emergent trees. Sabah's tropical rainforests are recognised to be of inestimable value and extraordinary beauty, and yet, they represent just a fraction of what was once common throughout Borneo - these last remaining stands of pristine forests are refuges for a great number of critically endangered plant and animal species.

Borneo's tropical rainforests are amongst the most diverse in the world. The island is home to an estimated 15,000 plant species, of which 10-12,000 are flowering plants - roughly 5-6% of the world's total. In Sabah and Sarawak alone there are an estimated 3,000 trees, 2,500 orchids and 50

The first light of dawn over the forests of the Danum Valley.

Pitcher Plant species, many of which are endemics and found nowhere else. Studies have estimated the number of fungi species from just a single location in Sarawak at over 8,000. Animal diversity is similarly extraordinary. Across Borneo as a whole, there are 622 species of bird, 154 species of snake, 92 bat species, 3-4,000 moths and 221 land mammal species. A great many of these species are endemic to Borneo and in some cases, threatened by extinction in other locations. Borneo and, in particular, Sabah's conservation areas, represent a haven for many species.

How do so many different species coexist together within these forests? The modern day forest community as we see it is composed of different species that have evolved together and formed a closely woven web of interactions - an ecosystem. The current biodiversity is simply a snapshot of this ecosystem's continual evolution as the physical conditions and interactions between species change over time. Sabah's forests are part of the greater Indo-Malayan rainforest region and are characterised by a steady temperature and high levels of rainfall. They are thought to have first developed over 140 million years ago and were little affected during the Pleistocene ice age. Borneo itself was cut off from the rest of SE Asia at the end of this ice age, over 10,000 years ago. As such, the physical conditions within Borneo's forests have been stable for a great length of time - suitable conditions for evolution and speciation.

In part, speciation and the creation of diversity may be a product of the sheer size and scale of the rainforest. Descending from the brightly lit, breezy canopy, through the branches and different layers to the shadowed, humid forest floor, it is very obvious that physical conditions change dramatically. Further differences in exposure, soil type and topography, as well as the complex three dimensional space that is the physical structure of the forest itself, result in an incredible number of microhabitats and, in turn, ecological niches. Over time, species evolve to occupy these diverse niches - new species are born, coexisting in time and space and yet separated by slight differences in the characteristics of the particular niche each species calls its own. Furthermore, as new species evolve, new interactions are created, driving forward evolution once again in an explosion of specialisation and speciation. The result is the wonderful diversity we see today in Sabah's forests.

Mosses and other epiphytes decorating the trees of the forest, Danum Valley.

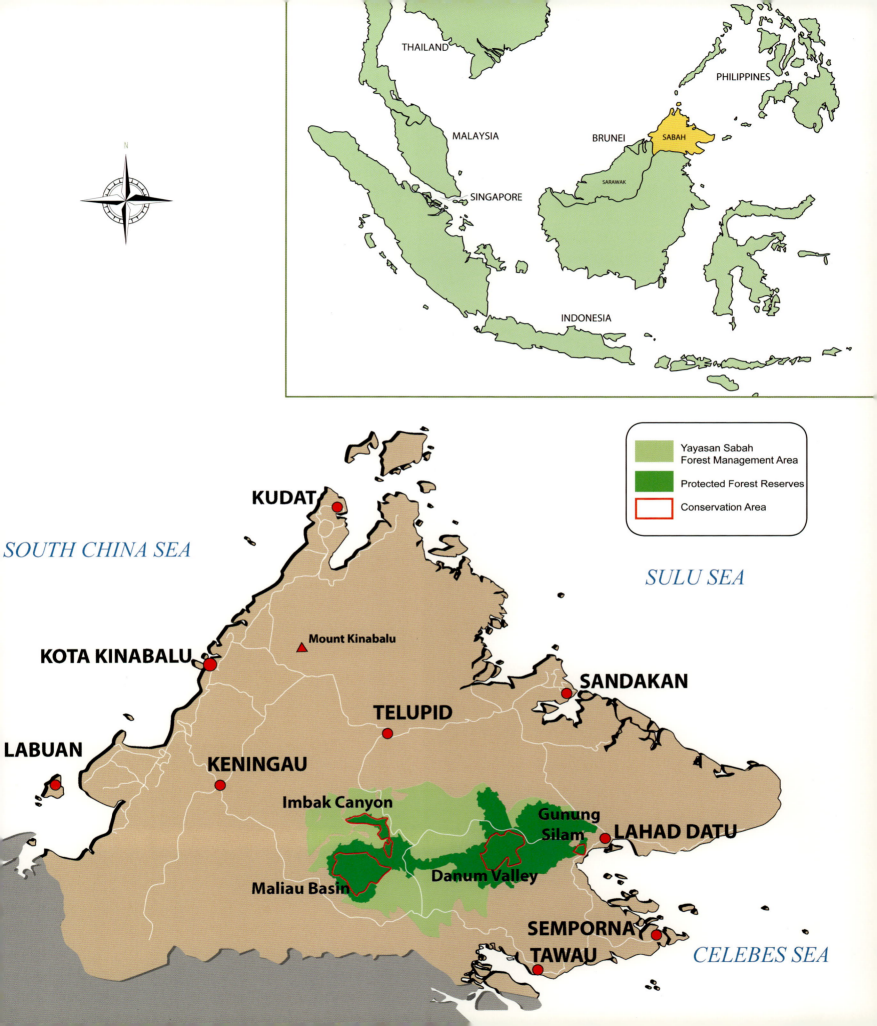

A first time visitor to a tropical forest may be overwhelmed by this diversity - at first glance, the forest seems to be an impenetrable, chaotic wall of tangled creepers, dense shrubbery and lofty emergent trees, arranged without rhyme or reason. However first glances can be misleading - it is only at boundaries alongside rivers and roads, or at gaps in the forest where light can penetrate, does such an abundance of creepers and climbers grow. Once beneath the canopy, the true structure of the forest reveals itself.

After the dense foliage of the boundary, the most striking thing about the forest is how open it is - very little light filters through the canopy above and so relatively few plants are able to grow on the forest floor. Most of the life and activity is above, up in the canopy where the trees spread their branches and leaves to capture light for photosynthesis. In fact, many species of rainforest plants have evolved strategies to take advantage of any sudden changes in the availability of sunlight, or use other plants to bootstrap themselves up into the canopy. For instance, when a large tree dies and falls to the ground, the resulting gap in the canopy creates a sudden flood of light into the dim understory layers and forest floor. Seeds and seedlings that have lain dormant spring into life, growing as fast as they can up towards the source of light. An entire suite of different species - grasses,

A Mengaris tree (*Koompassia excelsa*), a common emergent of the forest, Danum Valley.

climbers, creepers, shrubs and tree saplings - soon covers the forest floor in a carpet of green, all fighting each other for space and a share of the light. The winners of this 'fight for light', those that grow the fastest and out compete their new neighbours, eventually grow up into the canopy and seal the gap, returning the forest floor to twilight once again.

Other species such as lianas use trees to hoist themselves up into the light. Lianas start off as self-supporting seedlings that latch onto a tree - the liana's trellis. As the liana grows up towards the light, it attaches itself to the trunk and branches of its supporting plant, eventually reaching the sunlight in the canopy. Along the way, the liana slowly changes the physical structure of its own tissues and eventually loses the ability to support itself - the vine is now fully dependent on its trellis for support.

As a visitor gets used to the dim light and plethora of species, other differences in the forest will slowly become apparent, in particular, the different types of plants that are present and the structure of the forest. Changes in physical conditions such as exposure, soil type and altitude help to determine what type of community can grow at any one point whilst ecological processes

Green Mantis (*Heirodula* sp.), Danum Valley.

such as the creation of canopy gaps and the resulting forest succession will produce local changes in floristic composition. The sum of these different physical and ecological factors control what type of mature forest eventually grows and in Sabah's 'Green Heart' these different communities can be characterised into three broad types.

The most well known is the dipterocarp forest, a towering community of different tree species that closely resembles our perception of a tropical rainforest - the archetypal 'jungle' of our imagination. These forests are normally found on flood-free land below 700 m and if left undisturbed, can grow to extraordinary heights - Borneo is home to the tallest tropical forests on the planet. Within Sabah, these dipterocarp forests play host to the greatest plant and animal diversity and are of huge economic importance. Their value is essentially priceless, and conservation a real priority.

Heath forest growing on a ridge above the Imbak Canyon.

Dipterocarp forests are characterised by an irregular, layered canopy of 40-50 m, with a few emergent trees growing up beyond the main canopy to 60 m or more, even to 80-85 m. The immense weight of these huge trees, mostly members of the dipterocarp and legume families, is supported by buttresses that spread across the thin soil of the forest floor, allowing the trees to withstand irregular storm winds that occasionally sweep across the forests. Whilst dipterocarps dominate in terms of numbers of individuals, other types of tree show a greater species diversity. For instance, legumes such as the striking Mengaris are common, wild relatives of important fruit species such as mangosteen and durian are spread throughout the forest and figs - known as keystone species because of their importance within the rainforest ecosystem - are both abundant and vital to the animals of the rainforest. Up in the canopy and exposed to the rain and sunlight, epiphytes - including beautiful orchids, herbaceous species and huge Bird's Nest Ferns - as well as Lianas, rattans and climbers drape the branches of the trees in swathes of leaves and flowers. It is here, up where the sun and rain has its greatest impact, that the diversity of the plant community in the dipterocarp forests is at its peak. These species are completely dependent on the particular microclimates and physical support provided by the vast dipterocarp trees - the very scaffold of the forest.

Much of Sabah is mountainous and at these higher altitudes, dipterocarps and legumes give way to other species, presenting a very different community known as the montane forest. In Sabah, the gradual shift from dipterocarp to montane forest occurs between 750-900 m. As air temperatures drop and exposure increases, the once dominant dipterocarps and legumes give way to oaks, chestnuts, laurels and myrtles, mangosteens and Rhododendron become more common and tree ferns develop along mountain ridges. The canopy height decreases and emergents become much less common. Higher still, in the upper montane, the large emergent trees finally disappear and climbers become scarce or even absent. Instead the now stunted forest plays host to different species of heathers and the mist-enveloped branches of the low canopy are draped in mosses, liverworts, lichens and orchids. This so-called mossy or elfin forest is one of Sabah's most beautiful sights and a stark contrast to the vast forests of the lowland.

Soils on the plateaus of Sabah's montane forest are sandy, acidic and of poorer quality than in the warmer lowlands. In this nutrient-poor habitat grows the last of the broad forest types found in Sabah's 'Green Heart' - the heath forest. The even canopy of the heath forest grows to 7-20 m and the trees are quite closely packed together - quite different to that of the lowland. Dipterocarps are scarcer here and instead the heath forest is dominated by species typically found in the montane forest - laurels, myrtles, oaks and conifers. In many places, the heath forest soil is overlain by a layer of peat, reflecting the slow rates of decomposition in the water-logged, cooler conditions and the lower numbers of termite species that can survive here. This peat, rich in tannic acids produced as a chemical defence by the plants of the rain forest, gives rise to the famous black water streams of the heath forest.

To cope with the lack of nutrients in the sandy, leached soils, some species of plants, such as Pitcher Plants, have evolved unique adaptations to ensure a steady supply of nutrients. Pitcher Plants are amongst Borneo's most famous residents and the heath and montane forests are particularly rich in these species. These unusual plants specialise in capturing small insects and even vertebrates within a narrow, vase-like structure filled with a watery liquid. A gland within the pitcher secretes a chemical known as a viscoelastic biopolymer that ensures any insect that slips into the trap will struggle to escape the sticky liquid, even after a downpour of rain. Once its victim drowns it slowly decomposes in the liquid, releasing nutrients that are then absorbed by the plant.

A Pitcher Plant (*Nepenthes hirsuta*) growing in Imbak Canyon's heath forest.

The extraordinary plant diversity found in the forests of Sabah's 'Green Heart' supports an equally diverse community of animals and other organisms. Although research and surveys of diversity are far from complete, it is thought that like Borneo as a whole, Sabah's forests have some of the highest terrestrial animal diversity on earth. In the Maliau Basin 270 species of birds, 86 mammal species and 46 amphibians have so far been found and at Danum Valley, 110 mammal species have been documented, a significant percentage of which are endemic to Borneo or threatened with extinction elsewhere. Many of SE Asia's charismatic mega-fauna can be found in Sabah's forests, including the 'big five' of Bornean Orangutans, Bornean Pygmy Elephants, Sunda Clouded Leopards, Sumatran Rhinos and the Malayan Sun Bears. In fact, the 'Green Heart' of Sabah is one of only two places on earth where orangutans, rhinos and leopards still roam free. At a smaller scale, invertebrate life is also highly diverse. At Danum alone, over 1850 moth species, 180 butterflies, 184 litter-living ants and 128 canopy ant species have been recorded and over 10,000 beetle species are thought to thrive in the forest. It is obvious that Sabah's forests represent a vital refuge for many important and endangered animal species in SE Asia.

This stunning variety of animals - both common and rare, large and small - play a vital role within the forest ecosystems. Over time, the plants and animals of the forests have evolved relationships with one another, from simple predator-prey relationships to elaborate mutually-beneficial symbioses - an entire spectrum of interactions that together create a web of life. For example, many different species of animal play vital roles as pollinators of plants. Figs have evolved highly specific relationships with tiny wasps, without which they cannot reproduce, and many dipterocarp species - the vast emergent trees of the forests - are pollinated by tiny insects, just a few millimetres long, known as thrips. Birds inadvertently pollinate flowers as they feed on sugary nectar, evolved by the plant for the very purpose of attracting their animal partner. Plants also use animals later on in their life cycles, to help disperse their seeds. The most obvious method is through the production of nutritious fruit, within which the plant embeds its seeds. After being eaten by an animal, the seeds pass through the digestive system unharmed and are deposited elsewhere - amongst a fertilising mound of dung. Primates such as gibbons and orangutans are important rainforest seed dispersal species. Flying Foxes, the world's largest bats, are similarly vital to the plants of the rainforest. A typical bat might travel over 30 km in a single night, eating up to one-and-a-half times its own body weight in fruit and depositing seeds via its faeces as it travels. Many such dispersal strategies have evolved by plant species that live within the forest, as the still air beneath the canopy means they cannot rely on the wind to disperse their seeds.

A Bornean Orangutan (*Pongo pygmaeus morio*) feeding on flowers, Danum Valley.

Other organisms complete the nutrient cycle within the rainforest by breaking down and recycling dead plant and animal material and returning the nutrients to the soil. Fungi and invertebrates play a huge role in this process and like the other residents of Sabah's forests, are highly diverse. There have been few studies of fungi within Sabah itself but at Gunung Mulu in Sarawak, over 8,000 species are thought to live in the forests. 93 termite species have been found at Danum Valley, the highest recorded total in SE Asia. These insects break down rotting wood and use enzymes or symbiotic organisms within their digestive systems to break down the cellulose. Despite their tiny size, insects such as termites play an enormously important role within forest habitats because they often form the bulk of animal biomass and as a result, have a strong influence over many ecosystem processes. Termites are also considered an important indicator organism - a useful measure of the health of an ecosystem - as they are at the centre of so many tropical ecosystems and are vitally important in decomposition processes. In fact the humble termite plays a central role in the nutrient and carbon cycles of Sabah's forests.

As well as being the source of much of Sabah's diversity, the forests also provide a number of vitally important services to mankind. The most obvious is soil protection - the roots of the plants hold everything in place and prevent the soil being washed away by heavy rains. In turn, intact forests help to protect

A fungus growing in the leaf litter, Danum Valley.

entire watersheds. Mature soils absorb a great deal of water like a sponge and act as reservoirs, slowly releasing the water over time. Thus at places such as the Maliau Basin, the river still flows even in times of drought. And by soaking up rainfall and slowing water run-off, the forests prevent floods - which can wreak immense damage downstream. Forests also act as long-term carbon sinks, absorbing carbon dioxide from the atmosphere and locking it up within the tissues of the plants through the process of photosynthesis. With our concern about rising atmospheric CO_2 levels and global warming, the importance of maintaining healthy forest ecosystems is obvious.

Sabah's 'Green Heart' has long been recognised as a vital source of diversity and as a provider of important services, however, as within other tropical forest areas around the globe, land conversion and damaging and unsustainable forestry practices have threatened the viability of this valuable resource. Fortunately, the government of Sabah recognised the importance of the state's forests at a very early date and established the Sabah Forestry Department in 1914 whilst Sabah was still under the rule of the British Borneo Chartered Company. The original purpose of the department was to simply collect royalties from logging operators but it soon evolved to include the better management of the forests. With the Forest Enactment of 1968 and Forest Rules of 1969, the department's role expanded to include the protection and conservation of the state's gazetted Forest Reserves. And with the introduction of Sustainable Forest Management practices at a state level in 1997, the department expanded its remit to better conserve Sabah's natural wealth.

Today the Sabah Forestry Department manages nearly half of Sabah's total landmass, approximately 3.9 million hectares. Over 50% of this land is now designated as forest reserve, park or wildlife sanctuary - in fact, 18% of Sabah (1.35 million ha) is now totally protected as Class I and Virgin Jungle Reserves in locations such as Ulu Segama-Malua, Trusmadi, Danum Valley, Maliau Basin and the Imbak Canyon. These conservation areas now protect the very heart of Sabah's diversity.

Sabah's forests are an essential economic resource, highlighted by the fact that no other part of the world has such a high diversity of commercially-important dipterocarp species. Over the last 30 years, the state has undergone rapid economic expansion, relying on the exploitation of natural resources to fund this development.

The 7-tiered Maliau Falls is one of the most spectacular sights within Sabah's 'Green Heart'.

A forest-covered ridge rises above the mists filling the Danum Valley at sunrise.

Over-harvesting of resources and accelerated land conversion for oil palm plantations has led to a loss of diversity and isolation and degradation of many forest areas - to the point where the viability of these fragments has been reduced. Recent research has suggested that such small fragments of degraded forest cannot naturally regenerate commercially-important dipterocarp species and has highlighted the need for pristine and continuous forest to be conserved alongside production forests.

In 2012 the Sabah Forestry Department embarked on an ambitious project to change the way the state manages its forest resources. In conjunction with the UNDP, a mixed-use landscape of timber production forest, industrial tree plantations, rehabilitated forest and conservation areas totalling over 261,000 ha will become part of a unique project, one that may well become a model for forest management in the future. This area of land connects the well-established conservation areas of Maliau Basin, Danum Valley and Imbak Canyon in the west, with Gunung Silam close to the coast in the east - a connected landscape spanning some of the most important conservation areas within Sabah. The aim of the project is to bring the different land use areas under a common management strategy so that biodiversity conservation, ecosystem services and resilience are brought to the forefront, whilst allowing for ongoing sustainable resource use - a long-term, financially self-sustaining strategy to conserve Sabah's forests. Striking a balance between conservation, habitat restoration and production within a landscape of continuous and fragmented forests and agricultural land will be essential if biodiversity is to be protected, and water supplies, carbon stocks, soils and other forest-related ecosystem services are to be maintained for the future.

Under the careful management of the Sabah Forestry Department, Sabah's forests - with their soaring trees and flourishing epiphytes, Pygmy Elephants, orangutans and humble termites - will be protected and become the 'Green Heart' of Sabah's future development.

All these efforts would not have come about without the relentless support at the political level, of the State Government of Sabah, and for that, we thank the Chief Minister of Sabah, Datuk Seri Panglima Musa Haji Aman, for having the foresight to make things happen.

DANUM VALLEY CONSERVATION AREA

Lying close to the centre of the Yayasan Sabah Forest Management Area, the Danum Valley represents one of the most significant conservation areas in Sabah and some of the best-preserved forests in Borneo. These stunning landscapes are vital for research and science, conservation efforts and ecotourism, and can justifiably claim to be the most important area within Sabah's 'Green Heart' - no other location in Sabah, or SE Asia for that matter, has been as thoroughly studied and can claim such a high diversity of animals and plants. Amongst the many species that call the valley home, it is Danum's populations of big mammals however - including Bornean Pygmy Elephants, Clouded Leopards and orangutans - that attract adventurous tourists into the valley's remarkable jungle.

The Danum Valley Conservation Area (DVCA) comprises 438 sq km of undisturbed lowland dipterocarp forest lying within a gently shelving valley. Most of the floor of the valley is at a relatively low altitude, averaging just a few hundred meters above sea level, whilst the rim of the valley climbs up to over 1000 m, reaching its peak at Gunung Danum at an altitude of 1093 m. The southern and eastern borders of the conservation area are delineated by the Segama River, with protected secondary forest lying further to the

The Danum Valley Research Centre and Segama River from the air. The primary forest lies to the west of the centre on the left of the image.

east, and undisturbed forest inside the valley to the north and west. The Danum Valley Research Centre is conveniently located at the edge of the river, with access via a suspension bridge to trails and research plots in the primary forest across the river. This centre provides researchers with suitable facilities and assistants for field research, whilst tourists can explore the rainforest with the centre's experienced guides. Many trails lead away from the research centre into the forest, leading to such highlights as the Tembaling and Purut Falls, and several observation towers have been built including a spectacular canopy platform that looks over the centre. Near the northern edge of the conservation area is the famous Borneo Rainforest Lodge, situated within a sweeping bend of the Danum River. This beautifully-appointed ecotourism project offers luxury accommodation and has many interesting trails and its own canopy walk built 25 m off the ground. From this aerial walkway, tourists can watch the dawn light burn through the morning mist whilst listening to Danum's own 'dawn chorus' of birdsong and the calls of gibbons.

The Borneo Rainforest Lodge, a luxurious resort in the northern part of the conservation area.

The valley's early history is essentially unknown as there are no records or descriptions of Danum, or any trace of permanent human settlements. The most likely explanations for this are the rapids in the upper sections of the Segama River, making travel into the valley extremely difficult, and the low quality soils found in the valley, which together prevented and discouraged any early travel and subsequent settlement. It is in fact difficult to see how or why humans would have visited in the past. This is one of the main reasons why the Danum Valley is so important for conservation - the lack of any significant human disturbance prior to its protection. Whilst there is no evidence of any permanent habitation, there have been several archaeological finds to suggest that humans did visit the valley in the past. For instance, tests on bones found at a burial site on 'Coffin Trail', just over the river from the research centre, have suggested the occupants were buried there over 300 years ago, whilst a shard of bone found close to Borneo Rainforest Lodge is thought to be over 250 years old. These fragments of past history most likely represent brief visits to collect valuable resources and hunt, or perhaps temporary migrations, rather than permanent settlements.

In more recent years, traders and hunters probably entered the valley searching for Gaharu wood or hornbill ivory, although there is still nothing to suggest any significant human presence in the valley. In the late 19th and early 20th Century, reports of alluvial deposits sparked a small gold rush on the lower Segama River but again, the Danum Valley remained isolated and untouched because of the difficulty of traveling upriver - names such as 'Dismal Gorge' and 'Mt Tribulation' are testament to the struggles faced by early explorers. In 1970, a large proportion of eastern Sabah - including the Danum Valley - was placed under the management of Yayasan Sabah (YS) as part of their Forest Management Area. Danum was originally designated as a Class II protected forest as part of the Ulu Segama-Malua Forestry Reserve but, realising the unique status of the valley, YS unofficially protected the area

Wooden coffins at a burial site close to the Danum Valley Research Centre. The bones found within are thought to be more than 300 years old.

The Danum Valley Research Centre provides facilities for visiting scientists and tourists who wish to explore the incredible forest in the conservation area.

the Danum Valley Rainforest Research and Training Programme and a partnership was formalised with the Royal Society from the UK. This led to the opening of the Danum Valley Research Centre in 1986 and finally, in 1995, the DVCA was formally removed from the YS forestry concession and protected as a Class I Forestry Reserve, under the continued management of the DVMC. Today, the DVCA remains embedded within the extensive Yayasan Sabah Forest Management Area - over 10,000 sq km of primary and secondary forest stretching from Gunung Silam on the coast, to the western edge of the Ulu Segama-Malua Forest Reserves, near the geographical centre of Sabah - and provides a focus for future conservation within Sabah's 'Green Heart'.

and blocked any commercial exploitation. Following a WWF recommendation in 1976 and further consideration by YS, the DVCA was informally established in 1981 and a year later, the Danum Valley Management Committee was set up as an inter-departmental government committee to preserve Danum Valley and its inhabitants, as well as develop a collaborative research programme at the then proposed research centre. In 1984, further steps were taken to conserve the area with the establishment of

The rugged floor and slopes of the Danum Valley are covered in towering rainforest, one the most diverse habitats on the planet. These represent just a fragment of what once covered much of Borneo - the vast, sprawling lowland rainforest of old. The majority of the forest at Danum is of a single type and thus the conservation area represents one of the largest continuous tracts of pristine lowland dipterocarp forest remaining in Borneo. The number of plant species that can be found here is extraordinary and even after nearly two decades of research, scientists have only just begun to understand the magnitude of this diversity. For instance, in just two small study plots in the valley, scientists

The suspension bridge at the Danum Valley Research Centre allows access to the primary forest on the far side of the river.

recorded 511 species of trees. In comparison, North America as a whole has around 750 tree species. So far, scientists have recorded nearly 1,500 species of higher plants in 562 genera and 139 families from Danum Valley, an extraordinary amount and a significant percentage of the total number of species found within Borneo.

On first impressions, the forest seems a chaotic tangle of creepers, tree trunks and leaves but, in fact, Danum Valley's dipterocarp forest has a number of distinct layers. On the ground can be found scattered herbaceous species, saplings and low shrubs that are able to grow in the dim light of the forest floor. Also very obvious are the vast trunks of the canopy trees and their buttress supports. Moving vertically upwards, we enter the understory, a layer of palms, more saplings and other shrubs dominated by members of the Euphorbiaceae and Rubiaceae families. Higher still we find the forest canopy where the huge trees of the forest spread their branches and leaves in the sunlight. At Danum Valley, the canopy is typically between 40-50 m high and, compared to rainforest canopies of the New World, is relatively uneven and rugged. Dotted across this canopy are the true giants of the rainforest, the emergent tree species. These literally tower over the other plants at Danum, typically growing up to 60-70 m or more. In fact, as well as being one of the most diverse, the lowland forest found at Danum is one of the tallest in the world and a few individual trees have been recorded at over 80 m in height. Dipterocarps dominate this emergent layer - 70% of the individual trees growing above the canopy belong to this family and for the canopy as a whole, this number approaches 80-90% of all trees. These dipterocarps belong mainly to the *Parashorea* and *Shorea* genera, whilst the remaining trees are members of genera such as *Koompassia*, *Diospyros* and *Durio*.

Other families of plants are equally diverse at Danum Valley. For instance, many different species of rattans, vines and lianas, climb their way up into the canopy from the forest floor using the trunks and branches of trees as support. Figs are particularly diverse and are vital sources of food for primates and birds in particular. Many wild relatives of commercially-important fruit trees can be found, including durian, rambutan and salak - the durian being well known to attract Danum's elephants. Within the canopy itself, an array of epiphytic species flourishes on the branches of the canopy trees. These plants - including mosses, liverworts, ferns, herbaceous species and orchids - are non-parasitic. Instead they thrive in the different microhabitats that arise within the complex, three-dimensional space that is the canopy itself. This area of the forest has been described as the 'last floristic frontier', filled with unknown species yet so difficult to access and survey.

The different layers of Danum Valley's forest are best appreciated from one of the observation platforms built up in the canopy.

At the edge of the forest, where light can penetrate to the forest floor, Danum's understory is thick with saplings and other plants taking advantage of the increased light levels.

Like its plants, the animals of the Danum Valley are fascinating in their diversity. From minute invertebrates to large predators, the inhabitants of the DVCA continue to surprise scientists and the valley has become renowned for its healthy populations of animals. In particular, the valley's larger mammals - including the so-called 'big five' of Bornean Orangutans, Sumatran Rhino, Sunda Clouded Leopard, Bornean Pygmy Elephant and the Malayan Sun Bear - can all be found within the DVCA and the wider area of the Yayasan Sabah-managed forests adjacent to the protected area. All of these big mammals require substantial tracts of pristine or near-pristine forest to maintain viable breeding populations, highlighting once again the importance of Danum Valleys's continuous expanse of untouched forest. These animal populations - like the forests that support them - are representative of what was once found across much of Sabah and Borneo as a whole, before man began to have an impact on these unique ecosystems.

Danum Valley is home to 10 different species of primate, including Maroon Langurs or Red Leaf Monkeys (*Presbytis rubicunda*).

Of the 'big five', Bornean Orangutans have the most substantial population within the Danum Valley Conservation Area and are the most likely to be encountered by visitors. Bornean Orangutans are distinct from the Sumatran Orangutan, the two species having diverged approximately 400,000 years ago. The exact number and density of orangutans within the valley changes with the seasons and prevalence of fruiting trees, but estimates made by counting their sleeping nests put the population of Bornean Orangutans at around 500 individuals within the valley - quite possibly the largest and most secure population of these beautiful primates left in the world. Unlike the other great apes, orangutans are mainly solitary, although groups of juveniles and young with adult females can sometimes be encountered. One of the best chances of observing an orangutan is during rambutan season when the trees in front of the research centre bear fruit. It is then quite possible to sit on the verandah with a coffee and watch an adult orangutan feed on fruits, not 20 m away.

Danum Valley's Sumatran Rhinos are without a doubt the most endangered animals within the valley's boundaries. Very little is known about these secretive animals, but from camera trap studies and by surveying their mud wallows, it is thought that perhaps 2 individuals live within DVCA, out of a surviving population of around 10 within Sabah. In March 2014, a female was captured in Danum Valley in an effort to boost a breeding programme, although to date no Sumatran Rhinos have been born in captivity in Sabah. It is unknown whether the size of the wild population is large enough to support breeding and so the capture of this female is a last attempt to boost the numbers of this critically endangered mammal. Sumatran Rhinos are thought to be already extinct in Sarawak and are known to be extremely rare in Kalimantan - scientists there had their first sighting for over 20 years in late 2013 - and as such, it is likely that the population within Sabah represents a last hope for these shy animals of the forest.

Like the rhinos of Danum Valley, Malayan Sun Bears are highly secretive and unlikely to be spotted by tourists. They are completely dependent on pristine lowland forest and like the other 'big five', Malayan Sun Bears require large home ranges in order to survive. Malayan Sun Bears are the world's smallest bear and are superbly adapted to life in the forest, with a wide ranging, omnivorous diet that includes fruits, other animals, plant material and especially insects such as termites - Sun Bears have evolved elongated front claws that allow them to rip open rotting trunks and termite mounds in their hunt for food. These bears also have a voracious appetite for honey and honeycombs, earning them the nickname of 'honey bears'. Habitat fragmentation is one of the biggest threats faced by Sun Bears as they are unable to survive in degraded forests and fragments of primary forest. Poaching is a significant problem as Malayan Sun Bears are targeted for

The canopy walkway close to the Borneo Rainforest Lodge - one of the best places within the Danum Valley for birdwatching.

their body parts and for the ugly trade in bear bile, whereby live bears are farmed for the contents of the gall bladders. This bear gall is thought to have medicinal properties and the demand for Sun Bears and other species has led to a loss of up to 30% of the populations throughout SE Asia, in just a few decades.

As well as these charismatic larger animals, Danum Valley is home to many other species - some big, some small, some beautiful, some not so, but all vital to the functioning of this healthy ecosystem. So far 121 mammal species have been recorded from the conservation area - 26 of which are endemic to Borneo - including 10 different species of primate. Apart from the Bornean Orangutan, these include macaques, slow loris, tarsiers, different species of leaf monkeys and Müller's Bornean Gibbon. If lucky, a visitor may spot the latter moving through the canopy but are more likely to hear the booming, territorial calls of female gibbons - a very common sound at Danum.

the least-known cats in the world, with few sightings and almost nothing known about its habits. It is thought to occur at very low densities in lowland and montane forest, but little else is known beyond what can be be extrapolated from camera trap images and the occasional fleeting glimpse in the forest.

The Danum Valley is justifiably famous for its bird species, and the conservation area attracts many birding tourists hoping to spot a Bornean endemic. So far 317 species have been recorded - around 75% of the total number of birds found within Borneo as a whole - 15 of which are endemic to Borneo. Several rare and endangered species are regularly seen in the valley, including the Great Argus Pheasant, Bulwer's Pheasant, several pitta species and the Bornean Bristlehead. The Bristlehead is highly sought after by bird watchers as it is endemic and the sole species of its family. This beautiful bird normally flies in small, noisy groups within the canopy and is often seen from the walkways and observation platforms at the research centre and the Borneo Rainforest Lodge. Throughout the forest can be found a wide range of flowerpeckers, sunbirds, spiderhunters, flycatchers, woodpeckers, barbets, nuthatches, malkohas, babblers, drongos, trogons, bulbuls and other species - bird watchers can happily spend weeks immersed in Danum's bird diversity. The Segama River running past the research centre is home to kingfishers and Oriental Darters, whilst dead trees along the access roads are often used as perches by serpent eagles and bat hawks. The research centre even has a resident Buffy Fish Owl that uses the lights of the car park and badminton court to spot its prey at night.

Other vertebrate groups are as equally diverse at Danum although there has been less research on amphibians and reptiles and species lists are far from complete. So far, 73 reptile species have been collected, including 12 endemics. Animals such as hard and softshelled turtles, agamid lizards, skinks, monitors, geckos and 36 different species of snake have all been recorded from within the valley. Beautiful snake species such as the Reticulated Python - the world's longest snake - are relatively common at Danum. These snakes are thought to be capable of growing to over 8 m in length, although such extremes are very rare. However, 2-3 m Reticulated Pythons are not unusual. King Cobras - the world's longest venomous snake - are also found within the forests of DVCA. King Cobras are not true cobras, instead belonging to their own genus. They are notorious for their bad temperament and aggression, although this behaviour is more likely to be a defensive reaction by a nesting female or one that feels threatened.

Amphibians such as frogs have been reasonably well collected at Danum Valley, with a total of 56 species so far recorded, including 26 endemic to Borneo. They vary in habit from frogs that are completely dependent on streams or rivers and never leave the water, to those that successfully live in the forest, and use small pools of water in tree stumps for example to reproduce. These

Other mammal species recorded within Danum Valley so far include other species of ungulates such as mouse-deer, Muntjac and Sambar Deer, pigs and Banteng, along with civets, porcupines, otters, a variety of smaller mammal species such as squirrels and mice, and 38 different species of bats. These flying mammals are incredibly important within the forest ecosystem, acting as pollinators for many plant species and as seed dispersers. Four other species of cats have been documented from DVCA, including such rarities as the Flat-headed Cat, Leopard Cat, Marbled Cat and the elusive Bay Cat. This last species is one of different frog species vary considerably in form, and a few have evolved incredible camouflage or unique behaviour to survive within the forest. For example, the Malayan Horned Frog has evolved near-perfect camouflage that allows it to blend in with the leaf litter of the forest floor. Wallace's Flying Frog - discovered by the famed naturalist Alfred Russell Wallace - has bright markings that would leave it vulnerable to predators, except for a unique adaptation that allows it to leap and glide down from the canopy to escape predators or to search for mates at small pools on the forest floor. These frogs do not actually fly, instead their long limbs, toes and fingers, combined with skin webs, allow them to parachute down from the canopy.

The invertebrate species count for Danum Valley is an ever-increasing figure of an order of magnitude greater than that for vertebrate species. So far, over 1800 species of moth and 180 butterflies have been found. Over 300 species of ant have been recorded - 128 from the canopy and 184 from the leaf litter. 93 different species of termite have been found - the highest number recorded in SE Asia. An estimate for the number of different beetle species is a staggering 10,000. So far, 97 species of just one type, the dung beetle, have been found and over 600 different species were recorded from just five, large epiphytic ferns from the canopy. These extraordinary numbers reflect the number of different niches and microhabitats that the smaller animals of the forest can take advantage of and underlie the importance of invertebrates in the ecosystem as a whole. They play absolutely vital roles in the recycling of nutrients and pollinating plants - without some of these tiny species, the giant trees of the forest could not survive.

One of the most beautiful and unusual of all insects found at Danum Valley is the Orchid or Walking Flower Mantis, a species of praying mantis that has evolved camouflage closely resembling the flowers of the orchids it commonly associates with. These carnivorous insects lie in wait amongst the flowers, essentially invisible to the moths and butterflies that are their preferred food. For naturalists and photographers, these beautiful insects are an extraordinary prize, especially given how their camouflage and behaviour is quite capable of tricking human eyes as well.

The pristine forests and different animal species of Danum Valley are of obvious conservation value - there are few places like Danum Valley left in Sabah, or Borneo for that matter, and this fact alone is sufficient reason to preserve the DVCA as it is. The valley represents the Borneo of old, blanketed in dense lowland forest, and is a last refuge for many threatened species that would probably face imminent extinction without the protection offered by this area. However, Danum Valley and the surrounding forests of the Forest Management Area offer something hugely valuable, above and beyond the simple fact of their extreme diversity. These forests are unique in that together, they represent

A Scarlet-rumped Trogon (*Harpactes duvaucelii*), a typical resident of the lowland forests of Danum Valley.

an exceptional opportunity for scientists to compare and contrast natural and degraded forests, study how they change after being impacted by man and how forests can be returned to a natural state after harvesting. It would be naive to suggest that all forests must be totally protected, that all areas must remain untouched - Sabah's forests represent an extremely valuable resource and much of the state's recent development has been built on the exploitation of its forest resources. In fact, the dipterocarp trees found at Danum Valley and in the wider area of the Yayasan Sabah Forest Management Area - 267 species in 9 genera - represent the highest diversity in a single family of large, commercially-important trees in the world. Nowhere else has such a range of economically-important tree species. Thus, what is important is to develop ways to minimise any impact caused by harvesting of forest resources and learn how degenerated forests can be rehabilitated to as close to a natural state as possible, conserving biodiversity in the process and ensuring a future supply of resources.

The burial site on the 'Coffin Trail', close to the Danum Valley Research Centre, suggests that humans did in fact visit the Danum Valley in the past, but there is no evidence of any permanent settlement.

The canopy platform close to the Danum Valley Research Centre. Facilities such as these are important for both researchers and tourists, allowing access to a very different part of the forest.

Towards this end, scientists based at Danum Valley and at the surrounding research projects have been studying how forest ecosystems are impacted when harvested using traditional logging techniques versus reduced-impact methods. They are investigating ways of rehabilitating degraded forests with seedlings and reducing the stranglehold of creepers that thrive in newly harvested forests, smothering the growth of tree saplings. Other groups are investigating how ecosystem services change in plots of degenerated forests, isolated forest fragments and along waterways - vital experiments that will guide future decisions regarding where and when logging should occur in the future. The Danum Valley and the surrounding forests represent a unique laboratory where science and conservation, training and research will help preserve the pristine forests of the Danum Valley, and all its remarkable inhabitants, for future generations.

Bornean Angle-headed Lizard (*Gonocephalus borneensis*) overlooking forest at Danum Valley.

MALIAU BASIN CONSERVATION AREA

Deep within Sabah's 'Green Heart' lies the volcano-like Maliau Basin, a truly astonishing ecosystem protected from the outside world by forbidding cliffs and escarpments. Hidden within are stunning waterfalls, dense forests, abundant animals and rare species - an isolated, self-contained microcosm of Borneo as a whole. The basin preserves a continuous range of different forest types - from lowland dipterocarp to upper montane moss forests - and is home to some unique plant communities found nowhere else on earth. And like the other protected areas of Sabah, these forests are home to a rich diversity of plants and animals, many of which are endangered or exceptionally rare. Together with the legendary Lake Linumunsut to the north, and the animal-rich, lowland dipterocarp forests of the Tembadau Valley in the southeast, the entire area makes up the Maliau Basin Conservation Area - Sabah's mysterious 'Lost World'.

From the air, the Maliau Basin resembles a volcanic crater blanketed in green forest, however the reality is slightly different. Whilst there are several ancient volcanoes in Sabah, the Maliau Basin is not one of them. Instead, the unusual circular formation is a product of tectonic activity and

The Maliau Basin Study Centre from the air. The MBSC lies at the southeast edge of the conservation area and acts as the gateway to the basin.

geological processes - the uplift, faulting and subsequent erosion of sedimentary rocks, laid down 9-15 million years ago when the entire area lay underwater as part of a marine delta. The basin is close to 25 km wide - 390 sq km - and surrounded by steep, outward facing cliffs and slopes that reach up to over 1000 m along the northern rim. At its tallest point at Gunung Lotung, the rim reaches over 1600 m and here the forest is cold, windswept and cloaked by clouds and mist. Within the basin itself however conditions are hot and humid, similar to other lowland areas within Sabah. The floor of much of the basin consists of concentric bands of different types of rock, creating a series of rugged ridges and steep valleys, whilst in the south a relatively flat plateau extends towards the Maliau Gorge. The entire basin represents a single water catchment, with many streams cutting through the bedrock and creating a complex, radiating drainage pattern that eventually flows out as a single river through the Maliau Gorge. Here it meets the Kuamat River and eventually joins the Kinabatangan, Sabah's longest river. Two different types of rock make up much of the basin - mudstone and a harder sandstone. These erode at different rates and over the course of centuries, erosion by Maliau's many streams has produced beautiful, multitiered waterfalls where the water flows over alternating bands of mudstone and sandstone. The most famous is the spectacular 7-tiered Maliau Falls, but there are many others including the Takob-Akob, Sabendar and Giluk falls.

There are no historical descriptions of Maliau Basin or any trace of human habitation in the past - in fact, it is thought that apart from annual hunting trips by local Murut people, and unfortunately some modern-day poaching, the basin has remained essentially untouched into modern times. The word 'Maliau' probably derives from the word for a bowl in the local Tagal Murut language- 'oliou' - thus it seems highly likely that local people were aware of what lay hidden beyond the Maliau Gorge. However, given the difficulty of access it seems reasonable to assume that humans had very little impact on the basin's ecosystem in the past. Maliau was 'officially' discovered in 1947, after a pilot almost crashed into the outer escarpment that he declared might be 'Taller than Mount Kinabaloo [sic]'. In 1970, Maliau Basin and Danum Valley were declared part of the Yayasan Sabah Forest Management Area and six years later, a research expedition from the Forestry Department tried to climb the northern slopes, but failed to reach the rim. A further expedition in 1978 turned back due to illness and so it was not until 1980 that explorers looked down at the basin in its entirety. This team was the first to successfully climb the rim of the basin and members described seeing hundreds of helmeted hornbills in a single tree and confident argus pheasants, watching them from the forest. These reports cemented the Maliau Basin's reputation as a 'Lost World' and encouraged further expeditions throughout the 1980's and 1990's. In 1981 an expedition was airlifted on to the northern rim by helicopter, followed in 1982

The steep escarpments that surround the basin have kept outside influence to a minimum, preserving the forests in a near-pristine state.

The Maliau 'Sky Bridge', close to Belian Camp, provides a perfect way to explore the forest canopy.

Including the major buffer zones of the Tembadau Valley and the area around Lake Linumunsut in the northeast, the entire Maliau Basin Conservation Area (MBCA) now covers 590 sq km and is entirely surrounded by the Yayasan Sabah Forest Management Area. Within the basin itself a network of small camps and trails spread out from the study centre in the south, giving researchers and other visitors access to the different types of forest and spectacular waterfalls scattered throughout the basin. Observation platforms and a canopy walk have been built - perfect places for birders searching for Bornean endemics - and adventurous tourists can even make the arduous trek up onto the rim of the basin, an experience not too dissimilar to Arthur Conan Doyle's 'Lost World' expedition.

Even after just a day spent trekking, it is very obvious how the forest changes across different parts of the Maliau Basin. The lowland forest is home to very different plant species to those found up on the ridges, whilst areas with more sandy soils support very different trees, for instance, compared to areas with soils rich in clay. In fact, the particular type of forest and different plant species that can be found at any location within the basin are determined by a number of factors - the topography, soils, weather and the past history of the site. Within the forest itself, vertical changes in carbon dioxide concentrations, temperature, humidity, sunlight, wind and exposure all produce a great number of different microhabitats that further increase the possible diversity. On top of these environmental factors, a continuous cycle of tree falls and canopy gaps produces even more local diversity as the winners and losers of the 'fight for light' are determined across the forest floor. These different physical factors and ecological processes have determined what we see today at Maliau Basin - the many different forest types culminating in the pinnacle of rainforest development in Borneo, the lowland

by the first expedition into the basin itself. In 1984 the basin was declared a conservation area by Yayasan Sabah and in 1988, the first major scientific expedition was staged in Maliau in conjunction with WWF. In the 1990's, new species were discovered, waterfalls located and a base camp built on the southern plateau. A second scientific expedition surveyed the south-western portion of the basin in 1996. Finally, in 1997, the Maliau Basin was declared a Class I Protected Forest Reserve and the limits of the conservation area were extended beyond the basin to include Lake Linumunsut and buffer forest and the escarpment to the north and east. In the same year, the interagency Maliau Basin Management committee was set up and given the task of managing the conservation area and direct its future. In 2002, work started on the Maliau Basin Study Centre, which has steadily expanded over the last decade until today, where it has become the focus for science and ecotourism alike.

The Nepenthes Camp - also known as the Camel Trophy Camp - was the first camp to be built in the basin and provides access to the montane and heath forests in the area.

dipterocarp forest. However, the basin's other forests are of equal importance and in many respects, are actually more interesting to science, as some represent unique assemblages of plant species found nowhere else in Sabah, and possibly the world.

These different forests can be broken down into 4 broad types - the dipterocarp of the lowlands, the lower montane found above 750-850 m, the upper montane above 1200 m and on the exposed rim of the basin, and the tropical heath forest. The range of altitudes found across the basin means that an uninterrupted spectrum of different forest types has been preserved in a pristine state, a situation unique in Sabah and one that underlies the basin's high conservation value. The MBCA's dipterocarp forests are found on the basin floor and outside the basin within the buffer forests and around Lake Linumunsut to the north. These forests support the highest diversity of plants species, as well as the tallest trees - the canopy is typically 25-45 m tall, with emergents reaching 60 m or more. So far over 70 species of dipterocarps have been identified here, mostly from the *Shorea* and *Parashorea* genera, whilst other families including legumes, kedondong, rattans and other climbers are equally diverse. This lowland forest is also very rich in fig trees as well many species of important fruit trees - wild relatives of mangoes, mangosteens, rambutans, durian and salak can all be found here. On the alluvial soils close to the Maliau River grow spectacular Belian and Mengaris trees, some of the tallest trees found in Sabah. These beautiful Mengaris - famous for their pale, smooth trunks - can grow to 80 m or more and are a favourite home for giant honey bees, who like to build their semi-circular colonies on the underside of the trees branches.

Within the dipterocarp forest of the Maliau Basin grows one of Sabah's most unusual plant species - *Rafflesia tengku-adlinii*. This Rafflesia is one of the smallest of this highly unusual group of plants and has only been recorded from the MBCA and further west at Gunung Trus Madi in the Crocker Range. Like all Rafflesia, it is parasitic on a species of liana and has a remarkable life cycle. The plant has no stem, no leaves and no true roots. Instead, its haustorium, or absorptive organ, grows directly within the tissues of its host and the only visible part of the Rafflesia is its flower bud, growing from the forest floor like a small, dark cabbage. After several months, this bud finally bursts open to reveal the spectacular flower that smells of rotting meat.

As the altitude increases, the forest gradually changes and at around 750-850 m, lower montane forest is found. Here the canopy is typically lower than that found on the basin floor and there are fewer dipterocarp species and fewer emergents. At this altitude myrtles, oaks, chestnuts and mangosteens begin to dominate the forest and more epiphytes grow in the canopy of the trees. At around 950 m and above, dipterocarp species start

Maliau's famous 7-tiered waterfall is a result of erosion by the action of the fast-flowing Maliau River over the course of centuries.

to disappear and climbers become much more scarce. Mountain ferns appear along exposed ridges and Rhododendron and conifers become more dominant - particularly in areas with poorer soils - along with a wide variety of myrtles and oaks. Above 1200 m, dipterocarp species disappear completely and the forest takes on a stunted appearance in the exposed conditions of the ridges. Ferns, shrubby tree species, heathers and herbs dominate the low-lying forest, whilst mosses and liverworts blanket the forest floor and branches of the trees.

In montane areas with sandy soils, the last broad type of forest can be found - the tropical heath forest. The sandy conditions result in acidic, leached soils which support a very different type of forest with smaller trees and a lower, more even canopy, growing up to 20 m. This type of forest is also known as Kerangas forest, an Iban word used to describe areas that are unsuitable for growing rice. The poor, low-nutrient soils in the heath forest mean that many species of plants found here have evolved unique ways of surviving. Pitcher Plants are particularly abundant and 8 different species have been recorded from the Maliau Basin. Ant plants can also be found in Maliau's Kerangas forest. These unusual species foster a unique relationship with a type of ant in order to garner extra nutrients. At higher altitudes layers of peat build up on the forest floor, reflecting the lower diversity of termites and other invertebrates that are capable of breaking down and recycling the leaf litter in the lower temperatures and acid soils. Tannins leached out of this peat are responsible for the so-called blackwater streams found in many parts of the Maliau Basin.

Pitcher Plants (*Nepenthes reinwardtiana*) growing on the floor of Maliau's heath forest.

The mix of altitudes, exposure and soil types within Maliau means that many of the different forest types grow side-by-side, even intermingling in unusual combinations. Such transition areas are known as ecotones and they have given rise to some unusual assemblages of plants, including one that may be unique to Maliau. For example, the basin is home to oak-conifer forests,

A blackwater stream flowing through Maliau Basin's heath forest.

mixed Agathis forests and a Casuarina-conifer forest where the tropical heath forest meets the upper montane. Found on steeper slopes above 1200 m, this Casuarina-conifer forest is thought to be unique to the Maliau Basin and home to a previously undiscovered species of Casuarina. It is likely that this remarkable ecotone is found nowhere else on the planet.

To the untrained eye, these unusual forest types may not be so obvious or eye-catching, however the Maliau Basin is also home to a wide diversity of some of the world's most beautiful plants, including orchids. So far, over 80 species have been recorded from the MBCA, including several endemic species and rarities. Rhododendron, with their colourful flowers, are also highly diverse within the basin, particularly along the rim at higher altitudes and on the poorer soils of the heath forest. So far 21 species of Rhododendron have been identified, including some very rare species.

Like its plants, the animals of the MBCA are both highly diverse and abundant. Because of the basin's isolation, the entire area has been preserved in a near-pristine state and so populations of endangered animals are still relatively intact within the safety of the basin's rim. The protected lowland forests outside Maliau Basin are also vitally important for larger mammals such as elephants and banteng and the entire area is considered to be a refuge for many rare and endangered species threatened elsewhere.

Although surveys are far from complete, the MBCA shows levels of animal diversity close to those found at Danum Valley. Unsurprisingly, the highest diversity is found in the more productive dipterocarp forest of the basin floor - where the diversity of fruit trees is at its highest - and the number of animal species slowly decreases with altitude. So far 86 species of mammals have been recorded, including such critically endangered species as Sumatran Rhinos, Sunda Clouded Leopards and Malayan Sun Bear. 10 species of primate - including slow loris, Red and Grey Leaf Monkeys and Müller's Bornean Gibbon - can all be found within the basin itself or in the forests outside. Orangutans are known to live permanently within the lowland forest of the basin and on occasion, are seen in the heath and montane forests, although it is thought that most of these sightings at higher altitude are of transient groups visiting in search of fruit. Outside the MBCA, the forests of the Tembadau Valley protects healthy population of Bornean Pygmy Elephants and endangered Banteng - in fact, the valley takes its name from the Malay word for these cattle. It is thought that only 5,000 - 8,000 wild banteng exist across SE Asia, with a population of around several hundred remaining in Sabah. These beautiful cattle are threatened by poaching and habitat loss throughout their range, and hybridisation with domestic and feral cattle has led to contamination of the wild gene pool. The forests of the MBCA represent an important genetic sanctuary for this species.

Mammals such as Bearded Pigs are also thought to be abundant within the Maliau Basin, especially during synchronised fruiting events known as masting. Every few years, the majority of trees within the forest flower and fruit at the same time, producing an incredible glut of fruit. Bearded Pig populations increase substantially during these fruiting events and as a result, they are thought to undergo large-scale migrations across Sabah and down into Kalimantan in Indonesia in search of new sources of food. In 1986, a team of surveyors discovered the so-called 'Jalan Babi' - literally, the 'pig road' - within the Maliau Basin, a natural trail cut through the heath forest by the mass movements of hundreds or even thousands of Bearded Pigs during past migrations.

A stream flowing through Maliau Basin surrounded by dense vegetation. Streams such as this provide open gaps in the canopy for sunlight to reach the forest floor, enabling a multitude of plant species to grow.

Other large mammals so far recorded in the Maliau Basin include Muntjac, Sambar and mouse-deer, Marbled Cats, Smooth Otters, Malay Badgers, 14 species of squirrel and a wide variety of bat species. As the altitude increases, fewer and fewer mammals are found as many cannot survive in the colder, less productive montane forests. However, a few species are only found at the higher altitudes of the heath and montane forests, including a species of sculptor squirrel endemic to northern Borneo and the Tufted Ground Squirrel. The latter has recently been described as having the bushiest tail relative to body size of any animal in the world - an unusual accolade for this beautiful squirrel.

The bird species of the basin show similar patterns of diversity and distribution as Maliau's mammals, being more diverse in the lowland forest and in the Tembadau Valley, compared to the heath and montane forest. So far, 270 bird species have been recorded from the MBCA, including all 8 species of Bornean hornbills and all barbet species. This count is likely to be far from complete and scientists suspect the Maliau Basin is home to over 300 species of bird. Several endangered species have been spotted within the basin, such as Wallace's Hawk-eagle, Bulwer's Pheasant, the Large Green Pigeon, Bornean Bristleheads and the Straw-headed Bulbul.

Frogs and other amphibians are abundant within the Maliau Basin, especially along the many streams and the river. In total, 46 species in five different families have so far been recorded, including 25 from the heath and oak-conifer forest. Unusual frogs such as a Poisonous Torrent Frog and a tiny species of the *Kalophrynus* genus - that lays its eggs within *Nepenthes* plants - have been recorded. Another unusual species of frog thought to be found in the MBCA is the White-spotted Torrent Frog, also known as the Sabah Splash Frog. Unlike most frogs which use sound to communicate with other members of their species, this frog has evolved a unique behaviour that allows them to thrive in the noisy environment of rocky streams. Instead of vocalising, this frog waves its feet and hands at other males to make their territorial claims - an animal version of semaphore. Research at Danum Valley has shown that the males still make audible vocalisation to females, but the frequency of the sound has evolved so that it is distinct from the background noise of a stream or waterfall.

Records of invertebrate species are far from complete and scientists believe just a small percentage of the likely total has been described. The 1988 expedition found 33 species of butterfly, 74 moths - including such giants as the Emperor Moth - and 54 beetle species. More recent surveys have identified over 22 species of stick and leaf insects, and 37 species of butterfly and 29 different dung beetles were identified from within the heath and oak-conifer forests. Termite diversity varies caross the basin and whilst they are relatively scarce in the poor soils of the heath forest, they thrive in the richer soils within the oak-conifer forest. This is reflected in the number of species found - 18 from the heath forest and 33 different species from other areas.

The fabulous diversity of Maliau's inhabitants and the continuous range of forest types hidden within the basin are reason enough to preserve this extraordinary area. There are few places in Borneo where such pristine forest can still be found and fortunately, the Sabah government recognised at a very early stage just how important the basin really is. As part of the exploration of Maliau in the 1980's, one expedition in particular identified significant coal deposits. In 1991, an Environmental Impact Assessment was produced by a Canadian company regarding the proposed coal mining, stating that even with rigorous control of the mining activities, the extraction of this valuable resource would still have a significant impact on the basin and the Kinabatangan River downstream. Despite pressure to exploit the coal deposits, Maliau Basin's protected status ensured that the plans were eventually shelved and this incredible landscape and its inhabitants were protected for the future. Sabah's government chose conservation, rather than exploitation, for the remarkable Maliau Basin Conservation Area.

The nocturnal Malay Civet (*Viverra tangalunga*) is common throughout the lowlands of Maliau. It is a very successful omnivore, feeding on fruits, invertebrates and small animals.

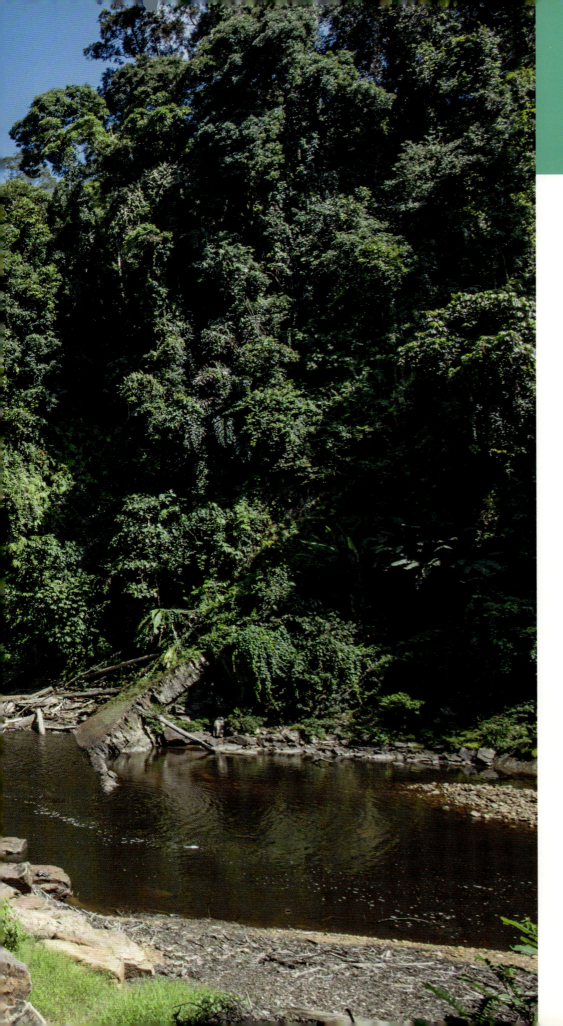

IMBAK CANYON CONSERVATION AREA

The Imbak Canyon Conservation Area (ICCA) is the smallest and least known of Sabah's major conservation areas and yet may well become one of the most important. This stunning landscape - with its rugged canyon walls and green-cloaked canyon floor - protects the largest continuous expanse of lowland dipterocarp forest in Sabah, as well as an extraordinary diversity of species, both plant and animal. It is an important refuge for the rare and endangered and may well be a source of new species and significant ethnobotanical riches. In the next few years, the ICCA is set to become one of Sabah's principle forest research and education facilities, with the development of a major study centre at the edge of the conservation area that will provide a focus for the continued exploration and conservation of this extraordinary natural wonder.

Both the Maliau Basin and Imbak Canyon are part of the same geological structure, and as such share a common history. They are made up of sedimentary rocks deposited between 15-20 million years ago when the entire area was part of a marine delta. Around 9 million years ago, these rocks were pushed up and folded by the forces of plate tectonics, then eroded away by the action of rivers and streams to create Imbak's steep-sided valley. Today the canyon is roughly 10 km long and enclosed by sandstone ridges on three

The beautiful Imbak Falls, just a few kilometres along the Sungai Imbak from the Tampoi Research Centre.

sides. At its widest point, it measures 7 km from rim-to-rim and runs in an east-west direction, roughly 50 km north of the Maliau Basin. At its lowest point in the east the floor is just 150 m above sea level however the sides of the canyon stretch up to 1000 m or more, reaching their pinnacle at Gunung Kuli in the south at 1380 m. The entire area is drained by two separate tributaries that run from the western and southern ends of the valley before merging to form the Sungai Imbak that flows along the eastern edge of the conservation area. In the rugged terrain south of Gunung Kuli, several streams drain the steep slopes before coming together as the Sungai Kuli, the southern boundary of ICCA. On the floor of the canyon itself, the river has eroded away alternating deposits of mudstone and sandstone, as well as the alluvial sands and gravels left by the river itself, creating a mixed terrain of short gorges, gullies and waterfalls, much like within the Maliau Basin. The most famous of these is the wide Imbak Falls - just a few kilometres along the river from the base camp - but another, equally beautiful waterfall can be found close to the Kuli camp in the south.

The ICCA was originally part of the Sungai Pinangah Forest Reserve, gazetted in 1965 and subsequently left in its original state due to the difficult terrain and proximity of other commercially-important forest reserves in the area. In 1984 the reserve was split in two - the Sungai Pinangah Forest Reserve and the Sungai Imbak Virgin Jungle Reserve, but once again no logging activities were carried out within Imbak. In 1992, the first expedition to the area was organised by the Sabah Forestry Department and Yayasan Sabah, although the team did not explore the interior of the canyon itself. The survey work carried out by this expedition led to a recommendation that Virgin Forest Reserve status be extended to include the floor of the entire canyon, not just the ridges to the north and south. Further expeditions in 2000 and 2004 studied the flora and fauna of the canyon in much greater

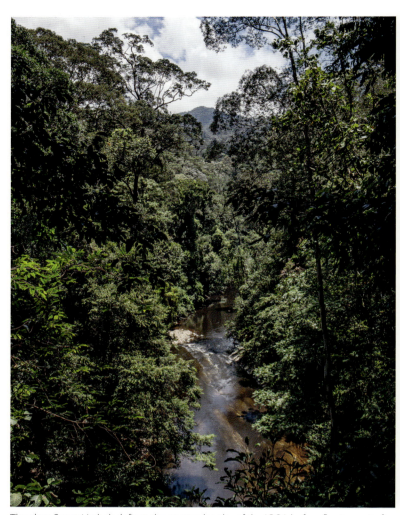

The clear Sungai Imbak defines the eastern border of the ICCA before flowing out of the canyon and towards the coast.

detail and subsequently, Yayasan Sabah informally set aside the area for conservation and science. Finally, in 2008 the government announced that the Imbak Canyon would be gazetted as a Class I Forest Reserve and completely protected for the future. In its current state, the ICCA covers around 270 sq km and is made up of the Class I reserve within the canyon itself, along with the Sungai Imbak and Batu Timbang Virgin Forest Reserves to the north and south of the canyon itself. The entire conservation area is surrounded by the Yayasan Sabah Forest Management Area, including the original Sungai Pinangah Forest Reserve to the north and west, and the Gunung Rara Forest Reserve to the south and east. Like Danum Valley and Maliau Basin, the ICCA is now managed by a committee that oversees the running of the area and is in the final stages of preparing the long-term management plan for Imbak - an exciting and vital step for this conservation area. Researchers and tourists can already access the conservation area and a network of trails and small camps has been established to allow exploration. These spread out from the Tampoi Research Centre, south to Gunung Kuli and west into the canyon itself, as well as up onto the canyon rim where small camps, such as at Bukit Beruang and Pinang-Pinang, give spectacular views over the canyon and towards Gunung Rara.

The Tampoi Research Centre from the air. The centre is a convenient base for exploring Imbak Canyon but will be superseded by the soon-to-be-built Imbak Canyon Research Centre.

The first light of dawn illuminates Imbak's forest canopy. The Imbak Canyon Conservation Area protects the largest intact swathe of lowland dipterocarp habitat remaining in Sabah.

Like the other conservation areas of Sabah's 'Green Heart', the pristine forest within the ICCA shelters an incredible diversity of plant and animal species. Imbak also shows evidence of high levels of endemism - probably more so than at MBCA or DVCA - highlighting its conservation value and importance as a centre for diversity. In particular, the plants found within the canyon seem to be especially diverse and a number of new species have already been described from the canyon.

Given their common geological history, the soils and forest types found here are similar to those within the Maliau Basin, and can be divided into three broad types. The dipterocarp forest of the canyon floor and sides covers over 50% of the conservation area and the forests below 250 m are thought to be the largest continuous expanse of lowland dipterocarp forests remaining in Sabah. This forest is dominated by commercially-important dipterocarps, especially those of the *Shorea* and *Parashorea* genus and, on the valley floor and along the river, has a typical canopy height of 30-45 m. Other common species here include Belian, the Bornean ironwood tree, and *Dryobalanops keithii* which can soar above the canopy to over 80 m in height. So far 79 species of dipterocarps have been recorded from the canyon area, 30 of which are endemic to Borneo, and many of the tree species so far described are rare or endangered elsewhere. To date, researchers have described two species of tree that are new to science - *Dipterocarpus megacarpus* and *Ceriscoides imbakensis*, from the Rubiaceae family - supporting the idea that ICCA is home to many endemic and unique species.

At 800 m and above, the dipterocarp forest gives way to heath forest. Here the soils tend to be more sandy and acidic and lack vital nutrients such as nitrogen, and so the forest that grows here is lower than that found on the canyon floor and supports far fewer emergents. Dipterocarps are still the dominant tree species but there are also plenty of others such as conifers and *Phyllocladus* sp., and mixed forests such as *Agathis* and oak-conifer - very similar to those found in the Maliau Basin. As the altitude increases to 950 m and above, the emergents completely disappear and a low, stunted forest, thick with mosses and epiphytes, clings to the exposed rim of the canyon. This montane heath forest is dominated by conifers and oaks and is known for its abundance of *Nepenthes*, Borneo's famous carnivorous Pitcher Plant.

The last type of forest is found at Batu Timbang in the southeast corner of the ICCA where a rather unusual forest grows on limestone. The difficult terrain of this eroded landscape cannot support large trees and mature soils only develop in sheltered gullies. As such the forest here has a very different assemblage of plants to that found elsewhere in the conservation area. Dipterocarps are still found, but are from the *Hopea* genus rather than *Shorea* or *Parashorea*, as is so common in Sabah's other forests. *Ficus*, *Pterospermum* and *Mallotus* species are also common in this unusual, but as of yet, little-known forest.

As well as surveying trees species, the 2000, 2004 and 2010 expeditions to Imbak examined other types of plant found on the canyon floor and rim. Together, they recorded 317 species from 84 families, 32 of which were endemic to Borneo. Today, the total species count is over 600 and scientists think that this number will continue to rise as the canyon is more thoroughly studied by scientists. As well as the dipterocarps, laurels, myrtles, legumes, palms and climbers are all abundant and diverse, whilst the forest floor is particularly rich in plants such as pandans. Gingers are exceptionally diverse, more so than at Maliau or Danum, and unusually, lowland and montane species co-exist in the same locations. Over 104 taxa of ferns have been found so far whilst the total for mosses currently stands at 115 species.

The number of orchid species from the ICCA is higher than that from Maliau and so far 196 species from 53 genera have been recorded, particularly from around the river and waterfalls. 20 of these species are new records for Sabah and 28 are endemic to Borneo. Scientists have even found a new orchid from Imbak - *Dendrobium jamirusii*. *Begonia* species are also very rich indeed and a new species, *Begonia postarii Kiew*, was described from Imbak just a few years ago.

The local communities close to the ICCA have long used the forests in the area as a source of food, income and natural medicine and the survey teams of all three expeditions interviewed members of the local communities to document the use of forest plants as medicines. So far, a catalogue of over 100 species of plant used for treating medical conditions such as stomach problems, skin diseases, headaches, pain and fever has been built up, with descriptions of how the plants are to be collected and used. Several of these species have already been shown to have various pharmacological effects and two - Tongkat Ali and Kacip Fatimah - have even undergone clinical trials to examine how effective these natural remedies really are. The local communities' knowledge of medicinal plants and their use demonstrates the importance of these forests and their value as sources of ethnobotanical remedies.

Imbak Canyon's intact forests provide invaluable ecosystem services, in particular by preventing the flooding of the Sungai Imbak, seen here from the air.

A juvenile Bornean Pygmy Elephant (*Elephas maximus borneensis*) with its mother and another elephant by the Sungai Imbak. Sabah's conservation areas are an important refuge for these magnificent animals.

The animals of the Imbak Canyon are thought to be less abundant compared to those found at Danum Valley. Populations of the big animals such as orangutans, Sumatran Rhinos and Bornean Pygmy Elephants are lower but the ICCA still represents a vital refuge for these endangered species. So far, 81 species of mammal have been recorded from Imbak Canyon, including many that are endangered. This total is likely to grow as more research and surveys are undertaken, and scientists believe that despite the lower abundance, the diversity of mammals within the ICCA is higher than that of the Danum Valley. The exception to this are the carnivores, which appear to be both more abundant and diverse. To date, 26 species of carnivores have been recorded from Borneo, 19 of which have been found in the ICCA.

Probably the most spectacular of Imbak Canyon's carnivores is the Sunda Clouded Leopard, recognised as a separate species from its Asian relative in 2006. This stunningly-patterned, nocturnal cat is incredibly secretive - little is known about its habits within the forest. It is thought to feed on birds and smaller mammals, as well as deer, pigs, porcupines and even primates such as orangutans, as unusually, the Sunda Clouded Leopard is at least partially arboreal, spending a lot of its time in the trees. It is the largest cat to be found in Borneo but despite its size, the Sunda Clouded Leopard is incredibly agile - eye-witnesses have described this cat descending head first down a vertical tree trunk and hanging and crawling along the underside of tree branches. It is obviously well adapted to life in the forest. This leopard requires a large home range to survive, but given that it is thought to survive in secondary forest, population levels within Sabah are relatively high compared to such animals as the Sumatran Rhino. Within Sabah as a whole, between 1,500 and 3,000 are thought to survive, although it is not known what percentage of these animals remain in large enough protected areas to support breeding populations. It is thought that the population of Sunda Clouded Leopards is higher in the canyon than elsewhere in Sabah.

Bornean Pygmy Elephants are also thought to be a separate subspecies, although here the evidence is less clear cut. Genetic studies suggest that these elephants diverged from their parent population around 300,000 years ago, but the lack of any fossil evidence lends support to a theory that the elephants of Sabah are actually descendants of individuals transported from Java or Sumatra a few hundred years ago. In either case, the Bornean Pygmy Elephant is typical of other Asian elephants, with a smaller body size and just a single prehensile 'lip' at the tip of their trunk. Their typical habitat is in the shade of lowland forests, but they also feed in more open areas such as along rivers or at the edge of the forest and like to make use of the roads and trails that run through the conservation area. It is not known how many individuals are found in and around the Imbak Canyon, however researchers have estimated that 1000 elephants roam throughout the Danum Valley Conservation Area and surrounding forests to the east of Imbak Canyon, roughly one third to one quarter of the total population in Sabah. They typically form small herds of 3-40 females and their young, with the males forming their own

Collett's Tree Frog (*Polypedates colletti*).

much smaller groups of adults. Bornean Pygmy Elephants require extensive home ranges to maintain healthy populations and the ICCA, DVCA and the buffer forests of the MBCA are an important refuge for this endangered species. Unfortunately, because of their roaming nature, these animals will sometimes enter commercial farming areas outside of Sabah's protected forests, leading to possible conflict with man - elephants don't distinguish between wild or farmed fruits when it comes to getting a meal. But as awareness of the habits of these animals increases, both at Imbak Canyon and further afield, it is hoped that such problems can be minimised in the future.

Surveys of birds within Imbak have revealed a high diversity of species, especially of lowland and montane species. 254 different bird species have been recorded so far including 6 different species of pittas, 20 flycatchers and many endemics such as the Bornean Treepie. The forest within the Imbak Canyon, the nearby conservation areas of Danum Valley and Maliau Basin and the production forests that connect these areas are big enough to support substantial populations of large, wide-ranging birds such as hornbills, one of Sabah's iconic birds. All 8 species of Borneo's hornbills are found at ICCA, including the commonly seen Rhinoceros, Oriental Pied and huge, Helmeted Hornbills. Like the larger, fruit-eating bats, these birds play a vital role within the forest ecosystem as distributers of seeds, particularly for species of figs. Research has shown that an individual hornbill will visit up to 240 different species of tree, feeding on the fruit and depositing the seeds elsewhere after they have passed through the hornbill's digestive system. Given that the home range of a large hornbill can approach 300 sq km, it is easy to see how important these birds are for trees.

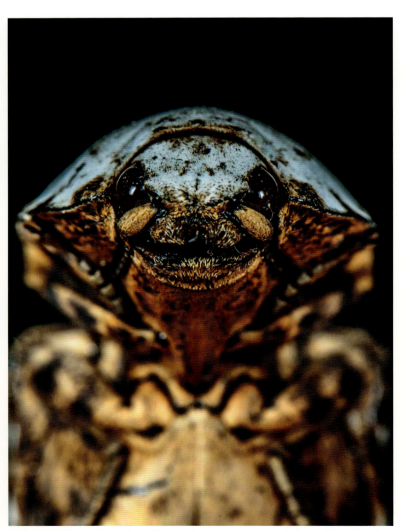

Click Beetle (family Elateridae). Click Beetles possess a spine which can be snapped into a corresponding notch on their body, producing a violent 'click' that can bounce the beetle into the air – a method used to avoid predation, but also useful when the beetle is on its back and needs to right itself.

The survey expeditions to the Imbak Canyon also examined populations of other animals, including amphibians, fish, reptiles and invertebrates. These teams of scientists found 38 species of amphibians and 33 reptiles, including rarities such as the Spiny and Malayan Flat-shelled Turtle. From the rivers within Imbak, 22 species of fish have been recorded - an unusually high number given the fact the watershed of the canyon represents a head water, a long way from more conducive habitats for fish. 175 different species of butterfly have been found so far, including several birdwing species such as the Rajah Brooke's Birdwing, named by Alfred Russell Wallace after James Brooke, the Rajah of Sarawak. Other groups of invertebrates appear to have levels of diversity similar to that found in the Danum Valley and the survey expeditions found a wide variety of different spiders and beetles, 30 species of dragonflies and 59 different aquatic insects.

The Imbak Canyon Conservation Area has extraordinary value as a centre of diversity and refuge for endangered and rare species, and the canyon's pristine lowland dipterocarp forest is the largest intact expanse of this forest type remaining in Sabah - reasons enough to conserve this unique landscape. Scientists also believe the conservation area could act as a vital climate refuge for the many species of Sabah's lowland forests during future climate change events. ICCA's range of habitats and altitudes, as well as its location in the centre of Sabah, means that if and when such climate change events occur, the forests within the canyon could remain intact and offer sanctuary to Sabah's different species in the face of changing climatic conditions. Imbak's pristine environment may also offer a unique opportunity to study how climate change impacts upon tropical forests - in fact, Imbak's self-contained and isolated canyon could represent a natural laboratory for environmental sciences.

Science and research at the ICCA is at a relatively early stage and the canyon's secrets are only now beginning to be explored. However over the next few years Imbak is set to become a major centre for research and education with the development of a significant field research centre to rival that found at Danum Valley. In partnership with Petronas, Yayasan Sabah will establish a programme of environmental education, public awareness, community outreach, research and ethnobotanical surveys based out of the soon-to-be-constructed Imbak Canyon Study Centre. This centre will serve as a research, training and education facility, and will provide accommodation for staff, researchers and visitors, classrooms, laboratories and a library. In addition, new research stations will be built within the ICCA and the existing camps upgraded to allow access for both research purposes and tourism across the entire ICCA. The knowledge and expertise that will grow from this partnership will guide future conservation efforts at this remarkable location, as well as across Sabah's 'Green Heart' as a whole.

The pristine, isolated forests of the Imbak Canyon are a perfect natural laboratory for studying climate change and its impact on tropical ecosystems.

GUNUNG SILAM

Sapagaya Forest Reserve is located at the far eastern end of the Segama Highlands, just 20 km southwest of Lahad Datu and 60 km from the Danum Valley Conservation Area. This forest reserve marks the far eastern border of the conservation corridor and, it is hoped, will become an important site for research and tourism in its own right. At its heart lies Gunung Silam, a low-lying mountain known for its unusual soils and beautiful forests, as well as high levels of endemism.

The gentle slopes of Gunung Silam rise 884 m from the nearby coast and whilst the mountain still retains its primary forest, the reserve is completely surrounded by secondary forest and plantations - in fact, Gunung Silam represents an isolated fragment of wilderness within a commercial landscape. The reserve was gazetted in 2009 as part of the wider Totally Protected Area and network, ensuring the protection of this mountain and its unique forests for the future. Today the reserve covers nearly 700 ha and has a number of trails that allow visitors to explore the forest around the summit, as well as the 'Tower of Heaven', a 30 m high observation platform looking out over the coast towards Darvel Bay and Lahad Datu.

Darvel Bay from the summit of Gunung Silam. The Sapagaya Forest Reserve is the most easterly of the four main conservation areas that make up the extensive conservation corridor.

At lower altitudes, between 200 – 330 m, the plant species of the reserve are similar to those found in Sabah's other lowland dipterocarp forests. The forest here has the tall canopy so typical of Borneo's lowlands - with emergents reaching to 50 m or more - and is dominated by dipterocarps of the *Shorea* genus. Other tree species, such as mangoes from the Anacardiaceae family, are also common on Gunung Silam. As the altitude increases the forest slowly changes and the dipterocarps show a dramatic drop in numbers between 610 – 700 m, completely disappearing after 770 m. At this altitude, other tree species such as oaks, myrtles and *Euphorbia* species start to become more common, whilst above 750 m, Casuarinas and evergreens dominate. As well as changes in the types of tree found, the physical structure of the forest also changes with altitude - the average trunk size decreases whilst the density of individual trees increases, typical of montane heath forests in Sabah. Close to the summit of Gunung Silam, the forest becomes a stunted, upper montane forest, thick with forest-floor bryophytes, mosses and epiphytes.

In other parts of Sabah, such stunted forest grows at much higher altitudes than that at Gunung Silam's summit. For example, on Mt Kinabalu near the west coast of Sabah, this type of habitat doesn't make an appearance until over 3,000 m. This 'altitudinal telescoping' has been observed at other locations around the globe and has been named the 'Massenerhebung Effect' - whereby similar types of vegetation occur at much lower altitudes on small mountains compared to on nearby, larger mountains. Exactly why this happens is still a mystery.

However, one possible explanation for Gunung Silam's unusual high-altitude habitat may be found beneath the floor of the forest. In fact, the reserve is unique within the conservation corridor in that the soils and rocks on which the plants grow are of a very different type to most of those found in Sabah. The majority of lowland dipterocarp forests grow on soils formed from sedimentary or metamorphic rocks, whereas Gunung Silam itself is ultramafic - made up of igneous materials similar to that found within the

Mist rising up from Gunung Silam's dipterocarp forest. The lowland forest on Gunung Silam is typical of that found in other conservation areas across Sabah.

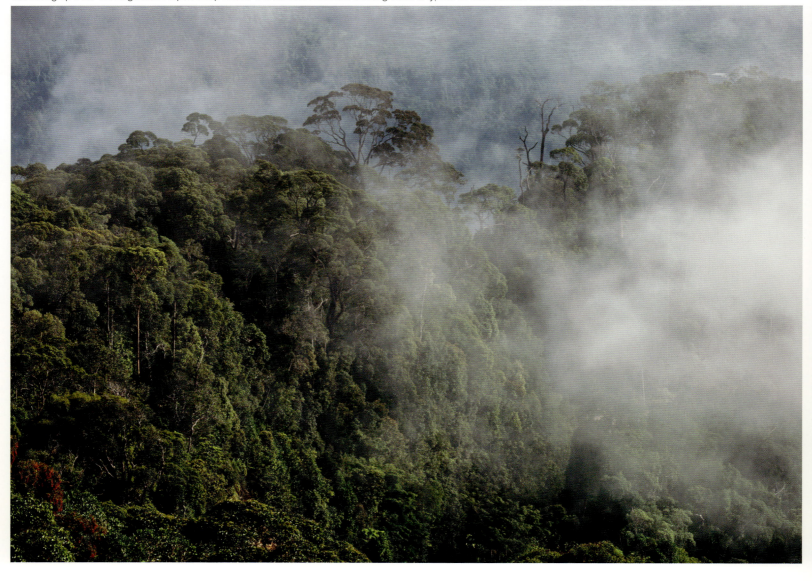

Ultramafic igneous rocks line a stream bed on Gunung Silam. These rocks are the source of Silam's unusual soils.

mantle of the earth. In other parts of the globe, such ultramafic rocks give rise to toxic soils, laced with high concentrations of metals. These restrict the growth of many species of plant and so the stunted or sparse forests that do develop are home to unique assemblages of plants and animals, often with a very high percentage of endemic species. Recent surveys on Gunung Silam have not found particularly high levels of the metals commonly found in other ultramafic soils, however an as of yet undiscovered element within the soil may prove to be the explanation for Gunung Silam's unusual stunted forests.

What is known is that the forests of this reserve are highly diverse and the few studies that have examined the plant life of Gunung Silam have revealed very high levels of endemism, as well as the presence of several rare and unique species. For example, scientists have found a new species of tree - *Syzygium silamense*, an evergreen - on Gunung Silam, as well as a tree from the Clusiaceae family - *Callophyllium sakarium* - that only grows on ultramafic soils in southeast Sabah, in particular on Gunung

Plantain Squirrel (*Callosciurus notatus*) foraging in a tree.

As the altitude increase on Gunung Silam, the dipterocarp forest is slowly replaced by montane heath forest.

Silam and several islands in the nearby Darvel Bay. A species of Rhododendron, *Rhododendron javanicum* subsp. *cladotrichum* was recorded in Sabah for the first time from Gunung Silam and the Pitcher Plant, *Nepenthes macrovulgaris*, was originally described from the mountain. Gunung Silam is also home to a wide diversity of orchids, including several species of minute jewel orchids. In fact, two species of these stunning orchids - *Corybas serpentius* and *Porbax borneensis* - were first discovered on the mountain. Both are endemic to Sabah and only grow in montane areas on ultramafic soils, such as those found at Gunung Silam.

To date, little is known about the diversity of animals on Gunung Silam as there have only been a few short scientific surveys focused on animal life. So far 23 species of mammal have been recorded, including many animals typical of lowland forest such

Close to the summit of the mountain, in the cooler, more humid conditions, the forest becomes thick with mosses and other epiphytes, typical of montane forests growing at altitude.

Opposite: Pitcher Plant (*Nepenthes macrovulgaris*) growing in montane forest.

Sunset over Darvel Bay from Gunung Silam.

as Bornean Gibbons, Pig-tailed Macaque, slow loris, pangolins, several shrew species, different squirrels, Malayan Stink Badger, Muntjac and Sambar Deer, Leopard Cats, palm civets, Bearded Pigs, flying squirrels and several bat species, including the rare Acuminate Horseshoe Bat. The guides at the reserve have recorded 167 species of bird, including a wide diversity of birds of prey - Black Eagles, White-bellied Sea Eagles, ospreys, Crested Serpent Eagles, Blyth's Hawk Eagle and Brahminy Kites have all been sighted on Gunung Silam. However, probably the most unusual animal found on the mountain is *Geosesarma aurantium* - a bright red, terrestrial crab that lives in the forest around the summit. This colourful invertebrate was first discovered on Gunung Silam in 1995 and is endemic to the mountain - it has yet to be found anywhere else.

With its protection as a Class I Forest Reserve, the future of Gunung Silam's forest and its unique species has now been secured. The reserve's potential for conservation, research, tourism and education can now be fully realised, and the mountain, with its beautiful orchids, endemic trees and unusual crabs, can rightly take its place as an integral part of the conservation corridor that stretches west from Gunung Silam, into the 'Green Heart' of Sabah.

A unique terrestrial crab (*Geosesarma aurantium*) found only on the forest floor of Gunung Silam's summit.

GALLERY

The 'Green Heart of Sabah' – view from the summit of Gunung Kuli of clouds covering the Imbak Canyon, with Mount Kinabalu visible to the north.

Clouds boiling up along the rim of the Maliau Basin. In the foreground are the pristine montane forests of the basin.

Previous page : Mists drifting over the remarkable 7-tiered Maliau Falls and pristine dipterocarp forest of the Maliau Basin.

Steep escarpments along the northern edge of the Imbak Canyon. This barrier has kept the interior of the canyon free from disturbances.

Next page: Danum Valley's mist-cloaked forest at dawn.

At first glance, Sabah's lowland dipterocarp forest seems a confusing tangle of creepers, trees and leaves of all shapes and sizes, growing without rhyme or reason. However, this habitat is actually made up of several distinct layers, each with its own assemblage of different tree and other plant species. Growing in the dim light of the forest floor are saplings, herbaceous plants, shrubs and climbers, all capable of surviving in the low light levels. Moving upwards, we pass through the understory - a layer of palms, more saplings and shrubs - before reaching the forest canopy, the dense ceiling of the forest created by the leaves and branches of the canopy trees. It is here, where conditions for growth are at their optimum, that we find the greatest diversity of plant species within these forests.

In Sabah's 'Green Heart', the trees of the canopy typically grow to 30-40 m, but these huge trees are themselves dwarfed by the giants of the forest, the emergents. These remarkable trees - mostly from the commercially-important dipterocarp family - can reach 60-70 m or more, and have even been measured to over 85 m in height. In fact as well being amongst the most diverse, Sabah's lowland dipterocarp forests are the tallest tropical forests on the planet.

The canopy of Danum Valley's dipterocarp forest.

Sunlight streaming through the forest canopy at Danum Valley.

The canopy of Sabah's 'Green Heart' - such as here in the Danum Valley - is dominated by a variety of dipterocarp species.

Previous page: A single Mengaris tree (*Koompassia excelsa*), emerging from the mists of the Danum Valley. This is one of the tallest tropical tree species with recorded heights of over 85 meters.

Unlike the even canopy of South America's tropical forests, the canopy at Danum Valley appears relatively rugged and uneven from above.

A large fern growing close to the crown of a Mengaris tree (*Koompassia excelsa*) in the Danum Valley.

Colonies of the Giant Honey Bee (*Apis dorsata*) in a Mengaris tree (*Koompassia excelsa*) at Danum Valley.

Bird's Nest Fern (*Asplenium* sp.), attached to the trunk of a canopy tree, Imbak Canyon.

Silhouettes of climbing plants draped over the branches of a tree, Danum Valley.

The canopy of Sabah's forests is a complex, three-dimensional space that is home to a significant percentage of the total diversity found within the forest. Some plant species growing here simply rely on the support provided by the branches and trunks of the surrounding trees, whilst others live their entire lives up in the canopy, without any physical connection with the ground below. The humid, sunlit conditions found here are perfect for plant growth and the many different microhabitats create a huge variety of different niches - perfect conditions for speciation. In fact, close to 10% of all vascular plants are tropical epiphytes that grow in forest canopies like those found in Sabah.

Epiphytes such as tree ferns are themselves ecosystems in miniature and support a wide range of other species, in particular invertebrates such as insects. For example, scientists in the Danum Valley have collected over 600 beetle species from just five of these ferns - a reflection on the total diversity that the canopy supports. In effect, the complex space and varying conditions within the canopy amplify the total number of species that can survive within this remarkable ecosystem.

Sunlight piercing through the trees at the edge of the forest, Danum Valley. Typically, the forest floor receives less than 5% of the sunlight that hits the canopy.

Epiphytic ferns growing on a tree alongside the Sungai Imbak, Imbak Canyon.

Narrow, curved buttresses radiating out across the forest floor, Imbak Canyon.

Angular buttresses supporting a dipterocarp tree (*Parashorea* sp.), Danum Valley.

Climbers growing up the trunk of a large tree in the Danum Valley. These climbers rely completely on the tree for support.

A large buttress of a dipterocarp tree in the Danum Valley, covered in epiphytes, seedlings, vines and climbers. The large trees of the forest provide a physical structure upon which many other species grow.

Coiled and knotted lianas growing in the Danum Valley.

The thin soils found beneath tropical forests provide very little by way of support and so many plant species have evolved unique adaptations to allow them to grow up into the sunlight, without collapsing and falling back down to the forest floor. For example, large tree species develop buttresses that are formed from specialised roots growing above the soil that are fused to the trunk at an angle, providing mechanical support and spreading out the weight of the tree across a much wider area of forest floor.

Some plants such as climbing Rattans and Lianas use other species to provide support. Both grow up from the ground like a typical plant and use hooks to attach themselves to other plants, or coil themselves around branches and stems, bootstrapping themselves up into the sunlight in the process. Strangler Fig trees on the other hand, use a slightly different strategy. Their seeds germinate up in the forest canopy after being deposited there in the faeces of birds. The young plant sends aerial roots down its host tree whilst simultaneously sending leafy shoots up towards the sunlight. As the fig develops the aerial roots can completely envelop the original tree, leaving behind a living, latticework structure when the host eventually dies.

Strangler Fig trees growing in the Danum Valley.

Moss-covered buttress roots on the floor of the montane heath forest, Imbak Canyon.

The thin trunks and tightly packed trees growing on a ridge in the Imbak Canyon are typical of Sabah's montane heath forests.

The stunted, tangled forest of Imbak Canyon's montane heath. At high altitudes and in poorer soils, the large trees of the lowlands cannot grow.

Maliau Basin's heath forest is a remarkable habitat, rich in unusual species such as Pitcher Plants, Rhododendron and orchids.

The rivers and streams of Sabah's 'Green Heart' play vital roles in these extraordinary landscapes and, in turn, are protected by the pristine habitats of the conservation area. Like the living ecosystems of the forests, the rivers vary according to the soils they drain, the rocks they flow over and the topography of the landscape. For instance, in the montane heath forests, blackwater streams - stained a dark brown colour by tannins leached from the sandy soils and peat - flow along rocky stream beds, whilst in the lowlands the rivers slow and their courses curve across alluvial deposits of gravel, sand and smooth rocks. In fact, the conservation areas are home to a complete spectrum of different types of water course - from headwaters with their rapids and waterfalls, to more mature rivers with pools and meanders.

The intact forests within the conservation areas help protect these watersheds by controlling the flow of water through the soils and by acting as reservoirs. The mature soils beneath these forests are capable of absorbing large amounts of rainfall and releasing it slowly over time, preventing flooding downstream. Once the trees and other vegetation are removed, the soils are quickly washed away and any rain quickly flows across the surface and into rivers and streams - causing further soil erosion and flash floods. This self-reinforcing cycle of erosion and flooding can only be prevented by preserving intact forests within the watershed, particularly on slopes and in headwater areas.

A blackwater stream flowing through Maliau Basin's heath forest. The water is coloured by tannins leached out of the peaty soil.

The rocky river bed of the Sungai Imbak near the Tampoi Research Centre, Imbak Canyon.

The Sungai Maliau with its waterfalls and rapids, Maliau Basin.

Two images showing Danum Valley's Sungai Segama during normal flow, left, and in flood, right. Intact forests, with their healthy soils, help to prevent excessive flooding by absorbing large amounts of rainfall and preventing run-off.

Previous page: Ferns (*Dipteris lobbiana*) growing in a stream within the Maliau Basin. These ferns are common throughout Sabah and have evolved narrow leaves that help the plant survive during floods.

Opposite: Aerial view of the Takob-Akob Falls, Maliau Basin.

The spectacular Imbak Falls are located just a few kilometres upriver from the Tampoi camp and research centre. These falls will be a focus for tourist activities after the Imbak Canyon Study Centre has been built.

Kuli Falls, Imbak Canyon.

Sabah's 'Green Heart' has the highest density of waterfalls in Malaysia, a product of centuries of erosion on alternating deposits of mudstone and sandstone, laid down across many parts of the conservation areas. The damp rock around each of the falls is a perfect habitat for epiphytes, ferns and amphibian species.

The Ginseng Falls, Maliau Basin.

The Giluk Falls, Maliau Basin.

The Sungai Segama close to the research centre at Danum Valley. The river here has deep, slow-moving sections which are more conducive to a wide range of fish life.

The still waters of the Sungai Imbak at a pool created by a tree fall and tumble of rocks, Imbak Canyon.

Small Javaen Barb (*Puntius orphoides*) in the Sungai Segama, Danum Valley.

Patterns of the forest - tree bark and lichen within the forest.

Dipterocarp trees flowering en masse during a masting event, Danum Valley.

Every few years, the forest canopies of Sabah's protected areas are painted in a mosaic of colours, as the dipterocarps flower and fruit en masse in an event known as mast fruiting. These irregular events can be highly localised or over entire regions and as of yet, nobody has worked out exactly how the dipterocarps - as well as many other species in the forest - time their flowering and fruiting together. One theory has suggested that mast fruiting is linked to droughts and the effects of El Niño Southern Oscillation events, but as of yet there is no conclusive evidence to support this idea.

A flowering dipterocarp tree (*Shorea* sp.), Danum Valley.

The bright flowers of a dipterocarp tree (*Parashorea* sp.) stand out against the dark green of the forest canopy, Maliau Basin.

What is known is that fruiting en masse has distinct advantages for the trees. In years with little or no fruiting, populations of animals that rely on the fruit will decrease, and these lowered populations are then easily saturated by the glut of food during the synchronised fruiting. The animals of the forest simply cannot eat all of the fruit and thus the trees maximise their chances of at least some of their seeds surviving and germinating. And by using an irregular cycle, the animals themselves cannot synchronise their own life cycles to match those of the trees.

Flowering ginger (*Zingiber* sp.), Maliau Basin. Gingers are diverse throughout Sabah's conservation areas, in particular within the Imbak Canyon.

Aechynanthus hians in flower, Imbak Canyon. These beautiful flowers are normally pollinated by sunbirds.

A flowering ginger (*Etlingera megalocheilos*), Danum Valley.

Begonia sp., Danum Valley

A Rafflesia flower (*Rafflesia tengku-adlinii*) growing in the Maliau Basin – the rarest of the 3 species of this parasitic genus found in Sabah's 'Green Heart'. Rafflesia are amongst Sabah's most unusual plants, and when in bloom the flower only lasts for 6-8 days – seen here towards the end of its bloom.

A Yellow-breasted Flowerpecker (*Prionochilus maculatus*) feeding on the flowers of a climber (*Poikilospermum* sp.), Danum Valley.

A Little Spiderhunter (*Arachnothera longirostra*) feeding on the flower of Torch Ginger (*Etlingera elatior*), Danum Valley.

A bee and several tiny insects collecting nectar from the flower of Red Beech (*Dillenia excelsa*), Danum Valley.

A Small-toothed Palm Civet (Arctogalidia trivirgata) feeding on Durian flowers, Danum Valley.

Opposite: A Long-tongued Nectar Bat (*Macroglossus minimus*) feeding on nectar produced by Durian flowers, Danum Valley. The Durian flowers only open at night when these bats feed.

Fallen petals from dipterocarp trees *(Parashorea malaanonan)* litter the forest floor during a mass flowering event, Danum Valley.

A dipterocarp tree (*Parashorea malaanonan*) covered in ripening seed pods, Danum Valley.

Dipterocarp seeds (*Parashorea malaanonan*), Danum Valley.

A dipterocarp's 'helicopter' seeds in flight (*Dryobalanops lanceolata*), Danum Valley.

Cauliflorous fruits growing on a vine of a climbing fig tree (*Ficus punctata*), Danum Valley.

A Green Iora (*Aegithina viridissima*) and ripening Rambutan fruit (*Nephelium lappaceum*), Imbak Canyon.

A wild Durian fruit (*Durio* sp.), Danum Valley.

Many different animal species play vital roles as both pollinators and seed distributors within the forests. Through the steady process of natural selection, plants have evolved colourful, scented flowers filled with sugar-rich nectar - designed to attract insects, birds and other animals that inadvertently cross-pollinate the flowers as they move from plant-to-plant. After pollination, seed-laden fruits are grown which provide a nutritious meal for an animal. The seeds then pass through the digestive system unharmed and are deposited - in a fertilising pile of dung - far away from the parent plant as the animal travels through the forest in search of food.

Other plants have evolved different strategies to help disperse their seeds. For example many dipterocarps used winged seeds that spin as they fall, slowing down their rate of descent and giving them the best possible chance to catch any winds within the canopy. The slower the seeds fall, the more likely they are to land away from their parent. When a squall hits the forests of Sabah's 'Green Heart', it is not unusual to see flights of these helicopter seeds drifting with the wind through the branches of the forest.

Rhododendron longiflorum var. *subcordatum*, Maliau Basin. A wide variety of Rhododendron - including several rare and endangered species - grow in the montane forests of the basin.

In many high altitude areas, Rhododendrons replace the once dominant dipterocarps of the lowlands, particularly along exposed, cloud-swept ridges and the montane heath forests. In fact, Sabah is home to a great many different species of these beautiful plants, including many endemics. The majority of these are found on the high slopes of Mount Kinabalu to the west, but the 'Green Heart' of Sabah also has its rarities, including *Rhododendron javanicum* subsp. *cladotrichum* which was recorded in Sabah for the first time on Gunung Silam.

Within Sabah, *Rhododendron javanica* has only been recorded from the Maliau Basin.

The orchid family, Orchidaceae, is one of the largest groups of flowering plants, with an estimated 25,000 wild species across the globe. Borneo alone has over 1,600 species in 160 genera - 40% of which are endemic - whilst 1,200 species have been recorded from Sabah. The majority of these are found in the montane areas between 1000 – 2000 m, particularly around Mt Kinabalu, but the lowlands and other habitats within the conservation areas of the 'Green Heart' also have an incredible diversity of orchid species.

Very little is known about the conservation status of many of Sabah's orchid species as a great many are epiphytes, growing within the canopy of Sabah's forests. This area has been described as the 'last floristic frontier' as scientists have only just begun to explore this habitat. What is certain is that as researchers continue to catalogue the rich diversity of species found within the canopy, the total number of orchids found within Sabah will continue to grow.

Grammatophyllum speciosum in flower, Imbak Canyon. These orchids can grow to incredible sizes and clusters weighing hundreds of kilograms have been found in Sabah.

Plocoglottis acuminata

Dendrobium cinnabarinum

Spathoglottis microchilina

Calanthe zollingeri

Bulbophyllum patens

Geesinkorchis altaticallosa

Dendrobium metachilinum

Cymbidium finlaysonia-um

Pitcher Plants (*Nepenthes tentaculata*) in Gunung Silam's montane heath forest.

Pitcher Plants are amongst Borneo's most famous plants species and the island is thought to be home to over 30 different *Nepenthes*. These carnivorous plants grow on nutrient-poor soils, particularly in the heath and montane forests, and have evolved a unique ability to trap and digest insects within their vase-like body.

Pitcher Plant (*Nepenthes veitchii*) Maliau Basin.

Pitcher Plant (*Nepenthes stenophylla*), Maliau Basin.

Pitcher Plant (*Nepenthes reinwardtiana*), Maliau Basin

Pitcher Plant (a natural hybrid, *Nepenthes stenophylla* crossed with *Nepenthes veitchii*), Maliau Basin.
Next page: A beetle trying to climb out from the slippery rim of a Pitcher Plant (*Nepenthes macrovulgaris*). Falling into the enzyme-rich liquid

Turkey Tail Mushroom (*Trametes versicolor*), Maliau Basin.

Inocybe sp., Danum Valley.

Akanthomyces sp. is an example of an entomopathogenic fungus - a parasite of insects capable of killing its host. The insect is first infected when spores latch on to its exoskeleton. These then grow and invade the host's body cavity where they feed on the internal organs, eventually killing the insect and developing a new generation of spores that emerge from the mummified body, ready to infect the next unsuspecting host.

A moth killed and mummified by a Clavicipitaceae fungus, (*Akanthomyces* sp.), Danum Valley.

Panaeolus sp. growing on elephant dung, Imbak Canyon.

Several species of fungus exhibit bioluminescence in Sabah's forests but the most commonly seen is *Mycena illuminans*, normally found growing on rotting logs as groups of small, white mushrooms. When these first develop, the glow is quite strong and the mushrooms can easily be spotted whilst walking in the forest at night, but as they mature and eventually die, the green, unearthly light fades away.

The glow is produced when energy from a chemical reaction is released as light - specifically, when a protein called luciferin is oxidised by enzymes known as luciferases in the presence of adenosine triphosphate and oxygen. Whilst researchers have a fairly good idea how the glow is produced, they are not so sure about why. These fungi glow 24 hours a day, constantly expending energy as a result, and so it must offer some advantage to the fungi. One theory is that the glow attracts flies, helping the fungi disperse their spores as the insects move around the forest. However, as of yet there is no real explanation for the eerie green light produced by these fragile mushrooms.

A bioluminescent fungus (*Mycena illuminans*) glowing at night, Danum Valley.

The coleopterans includes more species than any other insect group and accounts for almost 25% of all known animal species. About 40% of all described insect species are beetles (approximately 400,000), and new species are discovered every day. Some scientists estimate the total number of species of beetle to be close to 100 million, but a figure of around one million is more likely. These insects are found in all major habitats and are adapted to practically every kind of diet. Over 10,000 different beetle species are thought to exist within Sabah's forests, from the giant Rhinoceros Beetle, to minute species that live within Bird's Nest Ferns in the canopy.

A male Three-horned Rhinoceros Beetl (*Chalcosoma mollenkampi*) - Borneo's largest beetle, Danum Valley.

White Grub Beetle (*Lepidiota stigma*), Danum Valley.

Green Chafer Beetle (*Anomala* sp.), Imbak Canyon.

Violin Beetle (*Mormolyce castelnaudi*) on a large bracket fungus, Danum Valley.

Mating Tiger Beetles (*Calomera crespignyi*), Danum Valley.

Vividly coloured Tiger Beetle (*Cylindera versicolor*), Danum Valley. Tiger beetles are predators that actively hunt other insects using their accurate eyesight.

Longhorn Beetle (*Batocera rufomaculata*), Danum Valley.

Longhorn Beetle (*Batocera rufomaculata*), Danum Valley.

Longhorn Beetle (*Cyriopalus wallacei*), Imbak Canyon.

Longhorn Beetle (*Batocera lineolata*), Imbak Canyon.

GALLERY

Giraffe Weevil (*Cynotrachelus flavotuberosus*), Danum Valley.

Mantises or mantids are amongst the insect world's most spectacular ambush predators, and Borneo, with 118 species in 56 genera, has the highest diversity of these extraordinary predators on the planet. They are found throughout Sabah, predominantly in the lowland forests although some species have been found in montane areas. Mantids have evolved many different adaptations to increase their chances of capturing prey, including extraordinary camouflage that gives these insects the ability to blend into the leaves and flowers of their homes, and 'raptorial' front legs equipped with arrays of sharp spike to help them catch and hold their food.

To help them in their hunt, mantises have also evolved highly accurate eyesight. The insect's compound eyes are made up of thousands of ommatidia - tiny lenses and photoreceptors grouped together to produce the insect equivalent of a single pixel of visual information. The eyes are spaced apart on either side of the head, giving the insect a degree of binocular vision, and the prothorax and neck are articulated to allow the mantis to move its head whilst the rest of body remains still. Mantises are often seen rocking back and forth when hunting, a behaviour that is thought to further enhance mantises' ability to visually separate nearby objects - such as an approaching insect - from the background.

Top: Spiky Stick Mantis (*Toxodera beieri*), Danum Valley.

Centre: Orchid Mantis (*Hymenopus coronatus*), Imbak Canyon.

Bottom: Moss Mantis (*Majangella moultoni*), Danum Valley.

Top: Stick Mantis (*Paratoxodera* sp.), Danum Valley.

Centre: Indian Flower Mantis (*Creobroter gemmatus*), Danum Valley.

Bottom: Tree Bark Mantis (*Theopompa burmeisteri*), Danum Valley.

Dead Leaf Mantis (*Deroplatys desiccata*), Danum Valley.

Leaf Insect (*Phyllium pulchrifolium*), Danum Valley.

Leaf Katydid (*Temnophyllus* sp.), Danum Valley.

Camouflaged moth (*Lebeda cognata*), Danum Valley.

Camouflaged Katydid (*Zulpha perlaria*), Danum Valley.

Leafhopper (family Cicadellidae), Danum Valley.

Camouflaged Katydid (*Olcinia* sp.), Danum Valley.

Camouflaged Lichen Huntsman Spider (*Heteropoda boiei*), Danum Valley.

Many of the insects found within Sabah's forests have evolved extraordinary camouflage to help them avoid detection by predators or prey. Some resemble the leaves of the forest - dead or alive - whilst others mimic bark or wood. This camouflage is normally sufficient to fool human eyes and it can be extremely difficult to spot these different species unless they move and give away their position.

Camouflaged Giant Leaf Katydid (*Rhomboptera honorabilis*), Danum Valley.

Dead Leaf Grasshopper (*Chorotypus gallinaceus*), Danum Valley.

Lantern bug (*Pyrops whiteheadi*), Danum Valley. These bugs where so named when first described because they were thought to glow in the dark.

Lantern bug (*Pyrops tranversolineatus*), Danum Valley.

Previous pages:
Close-up of a katydid (*Dysmorpha obesa*), Danum Valley.

Close-up of a katydid (family Tettigoniidae), Danum Valley.

A cicada from the Cicadidae family emerging from its nymphal skin as a fully-formed adult with wings. The exuvia, or abandoned exoskeleton, remains clinging to the bark of tree, Danum Valley.

A mass of juvenile Leaf-footed Bugs (family Coreidae), Danum Valley. These brightly-coloured bugs display warning colours to advertise the fact they are noxious or toxic to predators.

Assassin bug (*Cosmolestes picticeps*), Danum Valley.

Many insects often adopt bright colours as a warning sign to deter potential predators, such as birds. Some species use bright colours to mimic the colourful flowers on which they live, while others use them to attract a mate.

Previous page: Tropical Swallowtail Moth (*Lyssa zampa*) Danum Valley.

The Saturn Butterfly (*Zeuxidia amethystus amethystus*), Danum Valley.

A pair of butterflies (*Charaxes affinis*) feeding, Maliau Basin.

Hawk Moth (family Sphingidae), Imbak Canyon.

The eyes of an unidentified moth (*Tasta* sp.), Danum Valley.

A Hawk Moth (family Sphingidae) amongst dead leaves, Gunung Silam. This moth has obvious eyespots on its wing - a deterrent to predators.

Next page: Slug Moth caterpillar (family Limacodidae), Danum Valley.

A Birdwing Butterfly caterpillar (*Troides* sp.), Maliau Basin.

An unidentified species of caterpillar, Danum Valley.

Cup Moth caterpillar (family Limocodidae), Danum Valley.

An unidentified caterpillar, Danum Valley. The caterpillars of many species of moth and butterfly are covered in hairs or spikes coated in chemical irritants, or simply taste bad. Their lurid warning colours are thought to advertise this fact to potential predators.

The ants and termites of Borneo are highly diverse and play enormous roles within the forests. Termites in particular make up much of the animal biomass of the forest ecosystem and are responsible for breaking down much of the cellulose found in dead plant material, retuning the nutrients to the soil to be used once again.

Golden Forest Ant (*Polyrhachis ypsilon*), Danum Valley

A column of worker Termites (*Hospitalitermes hospitalis*), Danum Valley.

Domatia from a species of Ant Plant (*Hydnophytum* sp.), or myrmecophyte, Gunung Sllam. Ant plants grow special chambers - the domatia - which shelter colonies of ants. In return for protection, the plant receives extra nutrients from decaying material brought into the chamber by the ants.

Asian Army Ants (*Leptogenys* sp.) on the move, carrying their pupae, Danum Valley.

Titan Stick Insect (*Acrophylla titan*), Danum Valley.

Gray's Malayan Stick Insect (*Lonchodes brevipes*), Danum Valley.

Spiny Stick Insect (*Haaniella echinata*), Danum Valley.

Sepilok Stick Insect (*Phenacephorus sepilokensis*), Danum Valley. This species of stick insect was first described from Sabah.

Close-up of a Lichen or Malaysian Huntsman Spider (*Heteropoda boiei*), Danum Valley.

Top left: Spiny Orb-weaver Spider (*Gasteracantha* sp.), Danum Valley.

Top right: Tarantula (*Phormingochilus* sp.), Danum Valley.

Centre: A Tarantula (*Phormingochilus* sp.) with her young, Danum Valley. Female Tarantulas lay their eggs in a suitable hole or crack in a tree and after they hatch, the young stay with the mother until large enough to survive on their own in the forest.

Bottom left: Tarantula (*Phormingochilus* sp.), Danum Valley.

Bottom right: An unidentified Jumping Spider (*Epeus* sp.), Danum Valley.

Giant Pill Millipede (*Glomeris* sp.), Danum Valley. These Millipedes roll themselves up into a tight ball when threatened, making it extremely difficult for a predator to break through the millipede's armoured exoskeleton.

Giant Pill Millipede (*Glomeris* sp.), Danum Valley.

A pair of Whip Scorpions (family Thelyphonidae), Danum Valley. Uropygids are closely related to true scorpions but lack the venomous sting of their relatives.

This small scorpion (*Chaerilus celebensis*) from Danum Valley was only recently described from Sabah and is thought to be endemic to Borneo.

Previous page: Golden Orb-weaver Spider (*Nephila pilipes*), Maliau Basin.

A Green Mantis (*Hierodula* sp.) feeding on a katydid, Danum Valley.

A Huntsman Spider (*Heteropoda* sp.) with its centipede prey wrapped in silk, Danum Valley.

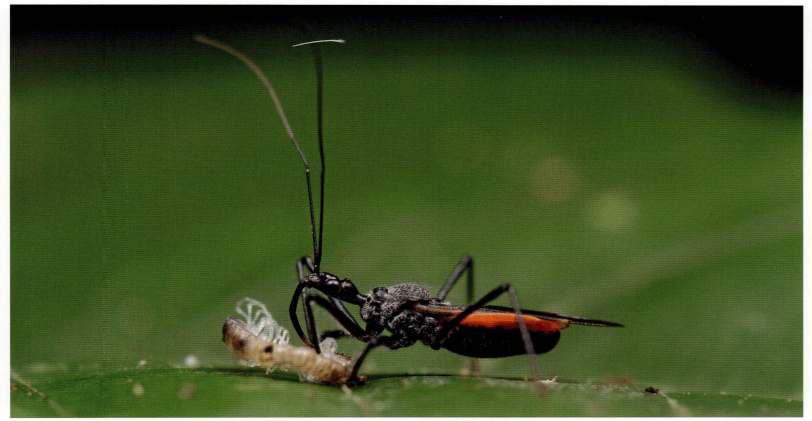

An unidentified assassin bug (family Reduviidae) feeding on a millipede, Danum Valley.

The predators of the insect world use a variety of techniques to capture their prey. Ambush predators, like mantises, rely on camouflage to remain undetected, adopting the colours of the plants in which they hide or mimicking dead leaves on the forest floor. Others, like spiders, spin silk webs to ensnare flying insects. Assassin bugs are equipped with a long, curved proboscis through which they inject a lethal cocktail of enzymes into their prey, which dissolves the tissues from the inside in a process known as extra-oral digestion - these bugs then simply suck up the juices, leaving behind the hollow shell of their meal. In fact, all rely on highly specialised behaviours and physical adaptations - the products of a million-year-old evolutionary arms race between predators and their prey.

Previous page: Harlequin Tree Frog (*Rhacophorus pardalis*), Danum Valley. Like several other frog species found in Sabah's conservation areas, this frog is capable of gliding from tree-to-tree, or down to pools on the forest floor.

Top: Frilled Tree Frog (*Kurixalus appendiculatus*), Danum Valley.

Bottom: Harlequin Tree Frog (*Rhacophorus pardalis*).

Opposite:

Top: Collett's Tree Frog (*Polypedates colleti*), Imbak Canyon.

Bottom: Rock Skipper Frog (*Staurois latopalmatus*), Danum Valley.

Frilled Tree Frog (*Kurixalus appendiculatus*), Imbak Canyon.

The frogs of Sabah's 'Green Heart' are as diverse as its other animals and to date, over 100 species have been found, living in nearly every major habitat type from the lowlands to montane forests. Borneo as a whole is home to over 150 species, over half of which are found nowhere else on earth - an extraordinarily high level of endemism. These different species vary in habitat and lifestyle, and surprisingly, on their dependence to water. Whilst some species spend their entire lives in streams and rivers, others only will return to reproduce, or rely on small pools of water or wallows to lay their eggs. Some species, such as Borneo's famous flying frogs are almost entirely arboreal, only returning to the forest floor to lay their eggs near small pools in foam nests. Others, such as the Malayan Horned Frog live in the leaf litter and have evolved remarkable camouflage that allows them to blend in with the dead leaves that cover the forest floor.

The majority of frogs found within Sabah are not considered endangered, however the loss of habitat could present a serious threat to these unique species as most cannot survive in commercial forests or cleared land. The use of pesticides, fertilisers and other chemicals may also threaten the frogs of Sabah, although little is known about the effect these chemicals may have on frog populations. However, none of the dramatic declines in frog numbers documented in such places as Central America, North America and Australia have been seen in Borneo and the future of these beautiful animals seems secure in Sabah's conservation areas.

Opposite:

Top: Spotted Stream Frog (*Hylarana picturata*), Imbak Canyon.

Bottom left: Lowland Litter Frog (*Leptobrachium abbot)*, Danum Valley.

Bottom right: Bornean Tree-hole Frog (*Metaphrynella sundana*), Danum Valley. As its name suggest, this species of frog lives in small pools of water within holes on trees.

File-eared Tree Frog (*Polypedates otilophus*), Imbak Canyon.

The Long-nosed Horned Frog, or Malayan Horned Frog (*Megophrys nasuta*), Danum Valley. This frog species relies on its incredible camouflage to remain undetected within the leaf litter on the floor of the forest.

A mating pair of Black-spotted Rock Frog (*Staurois guttatus*), Danum Valley.

A juvenile of an unidentified frog species, Danum Valley. The frog still retains the long tail of the tadpole stage and was found emerging from a small pool of water in a tree hole.

A male Rough Guardian Frog (*Limnonectes finchi*) carrying his tadpoles, Danum Valley.

As well as living in a broad diversity of habitats, Sabah's frog species have also evolved a wide variety of different lifestyles and reproductive strategies. Reproduction starts with mating and to do so, a frog must be able to locate a willing member of the opposite sex. Most frog species do this by calling to one another - the famous frog chorus that is known to anyone that has visited a pool or stream at night. The males use their calls to attract receptive females, as well as signal to other males to keep away from their territory. Some species living in relatively noisy environments near waterfalls use visual rather than audible signals, waving their arms or legs to attract mates or deter competitors.

After mating, the fertilised eggs are normally laid in water or, in the case of the flying frogs, in foam nests hanging above a pool. The eggs hatch out as tadpoles that grow in the relative safety of the water before transforming into adult frogs. One species, the Guardian Frog, lays its eggs in damp leaf litter or moss on the forest floor. After hatching, the tadpoles move onto the back of the male; he then protects and carries his young before releasing them into a suitable pool to develop further. Other species have become almost entirely independent from water. For example, the eggs of the bush frog are laid in damp moss and undergo the classic cycle of metamorphosis, from tadpole to tiny frog, entirely within the egg - the free-swimming tadpole stage has been completely removed in this highly unusual life cycle.

Ornate Earless Agama Lizard (*Aphaniotis ornata*), Imbak Canyon.

Sabah's 'Green Heart' is home to some extraordinary gliding animals, such as the Paradise Tree Snake (*Chrysopelea paradisi*), the Flying Dragon (*Draco volans*), Kuhl's Flying Gecko (*Ptychozoon kuhli*), Wallace's Flying Frog (*Rhacophorus nigropalmatus*) and the Sunda Flying Lemur (*Galeopterus variegatus*). Despite their names, none of these animals actually fly. Instead these species use skin webs, flattened bodies or elongated arms and legs to help them glide from tree-to-tree or down to the ground.

The forests of Borneo are home to more species of 'flying' animals than any other location on earth - 33 species out of a total of over 60 in SE Asia have evolved the ability to glide. In comparison, the forests of Central America have 2 'flying' species, Africa just a few and the Amazon none. Why do the forests of Borneo harbour so many gliding species? There have been several theories put forward but the most likely revolves around the dipterocarps that dominate these forests. These trees fruit irregularly and when they do, provide little food. Thus animals within Borneo's forests must forage far-and-wide, visiting many different trees in search of their food - be it fruit or other animals. Thus gliding would offer a distinct advantage, enabling animals to move from tree-to-tree without having to climb down to the ground and risk being exposed to predators.

Previous page: Draco Lizard (*Draco cornutus*) in flight, Danum Valley.

Opposite: Displaying Draco Lizard (*Draco cornutus*), Danum Valley.

Bornean Angle-headed Lizard (*Gonocephalus borneensis*), Imbak Canyon.

Bornean Angle-headed Lizard (*Gonocephalus borneensis*), Imbak Canyon.

Adult male Bornean Angle-headed Lizard (*Gonocephalus borneensis*), Danum Valley.

Peter's Forest Gecko (*Cyrtodactylus consobrinus*), Imbak Canyon.

Rough-necked Monitor Lizard (*Varanus rudicollis*), Danum Valley.

Beccari's Keeled Skink (*Tropidophorus beccarii*), Imbak Canyon.

Sumatran Pit Viper (*Parias sumatranus*), Danum Valley

Close-up of the head of a Borneo Keeled Pit Viper (*Tropidolaemus subannulatus*) showing the heat sensitive pit between the eye and nostril, Maliau Basin.

Spectacular pit vipers are amongst the most commonly spotted venomous snakes in Sabah's forests. They are named for heat-sensitive pit organs located between the eye and nostril on either side of their heads, which give these snakes the ability to detect body heat from prey animals. The pit organs have two chambers separated by a thin membrane, rich in nerve endings and sensitive to infrared radiation, and the positioning of the pits on either side of the head is thought to give these snakes a degree of directional range finding - the thermal equivalent of stereoscopic vision. As such, these snakes are capable of striking accurately in complete darkness.

Borneo is home to 6 species of pit viper, three of which are thought to occur in Sabah's 'Green Heart'. All of these lowland species have prehensile tails and are thought to be mainly arboreal and nocturnal. Pit vipers rest in the trees during the day, curled up around branches and sheltered from the hot sun. Then as the light fades they become active, using the combination of their thermal 'vision', sight and taste to search for small mammals, birds, frogs and lizards, or lie in wait for their prey to approach within striking range.

Opposite: Bornean Pit Viper, or Leaf-nosed Pit Viper (*Trimeresurus borneensis*) the only species of Pit Viper that lives on the forest floor, Danum Valley.

Left: Black-headed Cat Snake (*Boiga nigriceps*), Danum Valley.

Bottom: Oriental Vine Snake (*Ahaetulla prasina*), Danum Valley.

Common Mock Viper (*Psammodynastes pulverulentus*), Gunung Silam.

Juvenile Elegant Bronzeback Snake (*Dendrelaphis formosus*), Maliau Basin.

Juvenile Blue-necked Water Snake (*Macropisthodon rhodomelas*), Danum Valley.

Red-sided Keelback Snake (*Xenochropis trianguligerus*), Danum Valley.

Opposite: The head of a Reticulated Python (*Python reticulatus*) - the world's longest snake, Danum Valley.

Malayan Flat-shelled Turtle (*Notochelys platynota*) next to a small stream in the forest, Maliau Basin.

Asian Forest or Brown Tortoise (*Manouria emys*), Imbak Canyon.

Borneo is home to 19 species of tortoises and turtles, including several marine turtles and two alien species that have been introduced as pets and subsequently escaped. Only one species of tortoise is found in Borneo - the Asian Forest or Brown tortoise. This large species can grow to over half a meter in length and weigh 20kg or more. The Forest Tortoise is almost exclusively vegetarian and lives in evergreen lowland and montane forests in isolated areas across Sabah. Like all tortoises, this species is completely adapted to terrestrial life - although it is also commonly seen wallowing in pools.

Malayan Soft-shell Turtle (*Dogania subplana*), Imbak Canyon.

Soft-shell turtles on the other hand spend all their time in the water and are named after their skin-covered carapace. Sabah is home to several species including the Malayan and Asian Soft-shell species. The Asiatic Soft-shell prefers slow-flowing, muddier rivers and lakes in the lowlands, and is replaced by the Malayan Soft-shell in rocky, fast-flowing streams in montane areas. Both species are carnivorous and feed on a wide range of insects and vertebrates. Most species of soft-shell turtles are threatened throughout their ranges as a result of hunting - these turtles are considered a delicacy and unfortunately, can be found in markets and restaurants across SE Asia.

Close-up of a Malayan Soft-shell Turtle (*Dogania subplana*), Imbak Canyon.

Black-and-red Broadbill (*Cymbirhynchus macrorhynchos*), Danum Valley.

A Black-and-yellow Broadbill (*Eurylaimus ochromalus*), Danum Valley.

Dusky Broadbill (*Corydon sumatranus*) carrying nesting material, Danum Valley.

Red-bearded Bee-eater (*Nyctyornis amictus*) with a Carpenter Bee in its beak, Danum Valley.

A pair of Blue-throated Bee-eaters (*Merops viridis*), Danum Valley.

Previous page: A Borneo Bristlehead (*Pityriasis gymnocephala*), Danum Valley. This species is endemic to Borneo and is often seen in small flocks within the canopy.

Top: Red-naped Trogon (*Harpactes kasumba*), Danum Valley.

Bottom: A pair of Chestnut-rumped Babblers (*Stachyris maculata*), Danum Valley.

Opposite:

Top: Striped Wren-babbler (*Kenopia striata*), Danum Valley. This species is described as 'near threatened' due to habitat loss.

Top right: Male Whiskered Treeswift (*Hemiprocne comata*), Danum Valley.

Centre left: Grey-headed Canary Flycatcher (*Culicicapa ceylonensis*) Danum Valley.

Bottom left: Asian Paradise-flycatcher (*Terpsiphone paradisi*)

Bottom right: Asian Fairy-bluebird (*Irena puella*), Danum Valley.

Bornean Banded Pitta (*Pitta schwaneri*) foraging in the sun, Danum Valley.

Blue-headed Pitta (*Pitta baudii*), Danum Valley.

Opposite: Black-and-crimson Pitta *(Pitta usheri)*, Danum Valley. Many pittas - including all three shown here - are endemic to Borneo.

Bushy-crested Hornbill (*Anorrhinus galeritus*), Danum Valley.

A family of Oriental Pied Hornbill (*Anthracoceros albirostris*), Danum Valley.

Sabah is home to all 8 species of hornbill found in Borneo, including 5 which are listed as 'near threatened' by the IUCN. Throughout their range, these birds are endangered as a result of hunting and habitat loss - the Helmeted Hornbill in particular is targeted for its casque, used to make valuable hornbill ivory. Although populations of hornbills can be found in secondary forest or commercial plantations, it is thought that these areas do not have enough suitable nesting holes or food and cannot support viable breeding populations of hornbills in the long-term. Thus Sabah's large areas of protected forest offer secure refuges for these magnificent birds.

The Bushy-crested, Helmeted and Rhinoceros Hornbills feed predominantly on fruit and play an important role within the forest by helping many different tree species to disperse their seeds. These trees embed their seeds within nutritious fruit on which the hornbills feast. After passing through the birds digestive system unharmed the seeds are then released, often many kilometres from the parent tree as the hornbills continue on their daily rounds in search of food. Their raucous calls and noisy wing beats are amongst the most iconic and easily recognised sounds of Sabah's forests and spotting a flock of these beautiful birds, soaring through the forest, has to be one of the highlights of a visit to Sabah's 'Green Heart'.

Top: Helmeted Hornbill (*Buceros vigil*) in flight, Imbak Canyon.

Bottom: Rhinoceros Hornbill (*Buceros rhinoceros*), Imbak Canyon.

Wreathed Hornbill (*Rhyticeros undulatus*), Danum Valley.

A female Black Hornbill (*Anthracoceros malayanus*), Imbak Canyon. The male of this species has a white bill.

Male Argus Pheasant (*Argusianus argus*), Danum Valley. To capture this image a camera trap was used as these birds are very shy and difficult to photograph.

Buffy Fish Owl
(*Bubo ketupu*)
Danum Valley.

Brown Wood Owl (*Strix leptogrammicus*), Danum Valley.

Crested Serpent Eagle (*Spilornis cheela*), Danum Valley.

White-fronted or Borneo Falconet (*Microhierax latifrons*), Danum Valley. This bird is one of the world's smallest birds of prey and is endemic to Borneo.

Long-tailed or Crab-eating Macaque (*Macaca fascicularis*) foraging along the Sungai Segama, Danum Valley.

Long-tailed or Crab-eating Macaque (*Macaca fascicularis*) leaping from a tree across the Sungai Segama, Danum Valley.

Previous page: Maroon Langur, or Red Leaf Monkey (*Presbytis rubicunda*) feeding in a fruit tree, Danum Valley. The Red Leaf Monkey is endemic to Borneo and can be found within the canopy of the lowland forest, as well as montane areas.

Juvenile Pig-tailed Macaque (*Macaca nemestrina*), Gunung Silam.

Female Müller's Bornean Gibbon or Grey Gibbon (*Hylobates muelleri*) with her young, Danum Valley. The booming territorial calls made by Bornean Gibbons are one of the iconic sounds of Sabah's 'Green Heart'.

Müller's Bornean Gibbon or Grey Gibbon (*Hylobates muelleri*), Danum Valley.

Maroon Langur, or Red Leaf Monkey (*Presbytis rubicunda*) feeding on flowers. Danum Valley.

Mother and baby Maroon Langur, or Red Leaf Monkey (*Presbytis rubicunda*), Danum Valley. Maroon Langurs are sociable primates, living in troops that roam across the canopy during the day, feeding on fruits, flowers and other plant materials.

A male Bornean Orangutan (*Pongo pygmaeus morio*) Danum Valley. The Bornean Orangutan has relatively larger cheek pads compared to the Sumatran Orangutan.

A male Bornean Orangutan (*Pongo pygmaeus morio*), Danum Valley.

The conservation areas of Sabah's 'Green Heart' support one of the most important populations of orangutan remaining in Borneo. These orangutans - *Pongo pygmaeus morio* - are thought to be a distinct subspecies to those from Kalimantan and Sarawak and a completely separate species from those found in Sumatra. Compared to the latter, Sabah's orangutans have heavier bodies, a broader face, shorter beard and are darker in colour. Both species of orangutan are superbly adapted to life in the trees and have evolved grasping hands and feet, and incredibly strong, flexible limbs to help them move through the treetops with ease. Studies have shown that their diet is highly diverse and it is estimated that an individual may feed on over 400 different types of food, including fruit, seeds, bark, shoots, flowers, insects, eggs, honey and even small animals. They have even been observed to use tools in the wild - orangutans have been seen using spears to catch fish, bunches of leaves as umbrellas and and a leafy pad to protect their hands from the spines of durians.

Orangutans face considerable threats throughout their range, particularly in Kalimantan and Sumatra where clearance of the forests that sustain these animals has had a huge impact on populations of these animals. It is thought that over 50,000 orangutans still remain in Borneo - 10,000 within Sabah itself - although numbers continue to decline. The population remaining in and around the conservation areas of Sabah are thought to be the most stable and best protected in the world. In fact, the forests of Danum Valley, Imbak Canyon and Maliau Basin may represent a final stronghold for these incredible 'Men of the forest'.

A female Bornean Orangutan (*Pongo pygmaeus morio*), Danum Valley.

A female Bornean Orangutan (*Pongo pygmaeus morio*) feeding on flowers, Danum Valley.

An adult female Bornean Orangutan (*Pongo pygmaeus morio*) holding a baby, with two juveniles, Danum Valley. Like all great apes, Orangutans give birth to relatively helpless infants which are cared for by the mother through a long adolescence. Typically, juvenile Orangutans will stay with their mothers for five years or more, learning the ways of the forest.

A juvenile Bornean Orangutan (*Pongo pygmaeus morio*), Danum Valley

Bearded Pig (*Sus barbatus*), Danum Valley.

Sambar Deer (*Rusa unicolor*), Danum Valley. Different deer species and Bearded Pigs are the most common ungulates found within Sabah's 'Green Heart'.

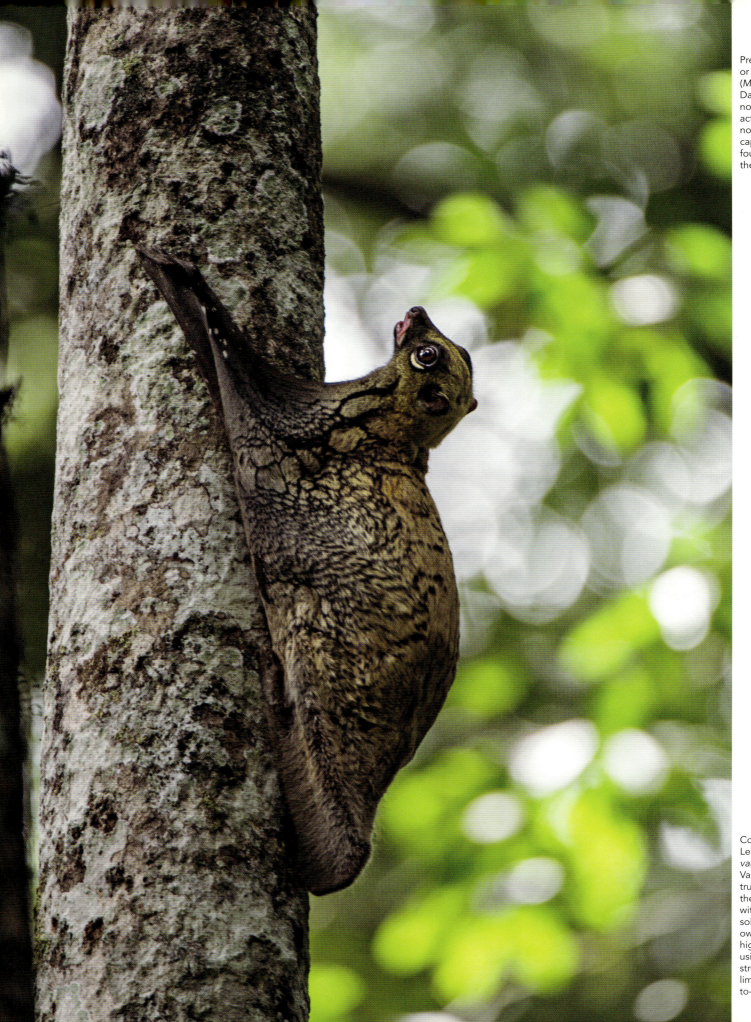

Previous page: Sunda or Malay Stink-badger (*Mydaus javanensis*), Danum Valley. These nocturnal animals are actually related to skunks, not badgers, and are capable of squirting a foul-smelling liquid from their anal gland.

Colugo or Flying Lemur (*Cynocephalus variegatus*), Danum Valley. Colugo are not true lemurs but instead the two species found within SE Asia are the sole members of their own order. They are highly capable gliders, using a skin membrane stretched between their limbs to 'fly' from tree-to-tree.

Western or Horsfield's Tarsier (*Cephalopachus bancanus borneanus*), Danum Valley. Tarsiers are carnivorous, feeding on insects and small animals that they hunt at night. Although they have very large eyes, it is thought that they actually rely on the sense of hearing to detect their prey.

Marbled Cat (*Pardofelis marmorata*), Danum Valley (camera trap image). This shy animal is thought to be at least partially arboreal but little else is known about its existence within the forest.

Previous page: A Malay Civet (*Viverra tangalunga*) foraging at night, Maliau Basin. Malay Civets are omnivorous and feed on invertebrates, small vertebrates, as well as fruit.

Masked Palm Civet (*Paguma larvata*), Danum Valley (camera trap image).

Most of the predatory mammals found within the forests of Sabah are extremely elusive and often nocturnal, making them very difficult to see, much less photograph. Camera traps - which can be left in the forest for weeks at a time and are usually triggered by an invisible infrared beam - offer the only real chance of getting a glimpse into the hidden lives of these magnificent animals.

Sunda Clouded Leopard (*Neofelis diardi*), Danum Valley (camera trap image). The Sunda Clouded Leopard is one of Sabah's most beautiful cats. Scientists believe that the Imbak Canyon and the surrounding forests protect a particularly large population of these cats.

Short-tailed Mongoose (*Herpestes brachyurus*), Danum Valley (camera trap image).

Feeding Bornean Pygmy Elephant (*Elephas maximus borneensis*), Imbak Canyon.

Juvenile Bornean Pygmy Elephant (*Elephas maximus borneensis*) playing in a river, Imbak Canyon.

Bornean Pygmy Elephant (*Elephas maximus borneensis*), Imbak Canyon.

The classification of the Bornean Pygmy Elephant has had a somewhat convoluted history. For many years, scientists believed these elephants were descendants of animals owned and released into the wild by the Sultanate of Sulu, the rulers over much of northern Borneo until the arrival of the British. However, recent genetic studies focusing on mitochondrial and microsatellite DNA has suggested that, in fact, these charismatic animals evolved from ancestors found in Sunda Land, a large area of dry land exposed during the last ice age that included Borneo, Java, Sumatra and Peninsular Malaysia. These ancestral elephants where free to roam throughout Sunda Land but as sea levels rose at the end of the ice age, over 300,000 years ago, the population within Borneo became isolated and has followed its own evolutionary path ever since.

Today the Bornean Pygmy Elephant is threatened by habitat loss and fragmentation but has found sanctuary within Sabah's conservation areas, in particular in and around Danum Valley, the Ulu Segama watershed and along the Kinabatangan river. It is hoped that with suitable protection now in place, the largest of Borneo's animals now has a secure future in Sabah's 'Green Heart'.

Sumatran Rhino (*Dicerorhinus sumatrensis*), Tabin Wildlife Reserve. This animal was part of a captive breeding programme at Tabin Wildlife Reserve and was photographed within the animal's enclosure.

Sumatran Rhino (*Dicerorhinus sumatrensis*), Tabin Wildlife Reserve.

Sabah's Sumatran Rhinos are perhaps one of the most critically endangered animals on the planet. These remarkable animals are now limited to just a few, scattered populations across SE Asia, and it is thought that less than a hundred rhinos remain in the wild. It is not known exactly how many rhinos remain in Sabah but estimates put the remaining population at just 10 individuals, 2 of which are thought to reside within the Danum Valley Conservation Area.

Since the 1980's, Sabah has attempted to boost the population of its rhinos, capturing several wild animals and initiating a captive breeding programme. Unfortunately, the programme has so far failed to produce a pregnancy - simply because so little is known about the biology and behaviour of the Sumatran Rhino. However, earlier in 2014, an additional female was captured and conservation biologists will attempt a new breeding programme using advanced reproductive technology. It is hoped that this last attempt will lift Sabah's rhinos from the brink of extinction.

FOREST MANAGEMENT

By Dr Glen Reynolds
Director, Royal Society South East Asia Rainforest Research Program (SEARRP)

Management history of the forests of the 'Green Heart' of Sabah

The rainforests of the 'Green Heart' of Sabah stretch in an unbroken, 200 kilometer swathe from the coastal forests surrounding Gunung Silam in the east, through the low-lying plains of the Ulu Segama and Malua Forest Reserves, the lowland and hill forests of Danum Valley and Imbak Canyon and west to the central Bornean uplands of Maliau Basin. This continuous corridor of entirely natural forest, unbroken by the plantations and settlements which have proliferated elsewhere in Sabah over recent decades, covers close to 5,000 sq km – an area more than three times the extent of Greater London, or about the same size as Brunei Darussalam.

Covering an altitudinal gradient from just above sea level in the east to over 1,600 m at the highest point of Maliau Basin, the 'Green Heart' of Sabah represents arguably the most ecologically-important forested area remaining intact on the island of Borneo. Although roughly two-thirds of the area has been selectively logged,

A scientist collecting samples from within a Bird's Nest Fern, high up in the forest canopy, Danum Valley. The canopy has been described as the 'last floristic frontier', and is home to a significant percentage of the total diversity found within Sabah's forests.

in some cases heavily, at its core are three pristine conservation areas of inestimable value - Danum Valley, Maliau Basin and Imbak Canyon. The forests of these protected landscapes - totalling some 1,500 sq km - have never been subject to any but the most inconsequential form of human disturbance and are now nested within, and fully buffered by, protected and recovering forests, thus securing their integrity and the biodiversity and other conservation values they support.

Humans in the forest

The areas which now comprise the Danum Valley Conservation Area, and much of the forest surrounding it, were, until recorded history, completely covered in undisturbed primary forest. There is little or no evidence of permanent settlements along any of the major rivers that traverse these forests – or any likelihood that

A truck loaded with large dipterocarp logs, ready to be transported to the coast. Sabah has the highest recorded diversity of these commercially-important trees in the world.

300 year old coffins at a burial site along the Segama River, Danum Valley. The majority of Sabah's conservation areas have been never been permanently inhabited by humans.

indigenous hunter-gatherer communities, so active elsewhere on Borneo, ever exploited the area on a regular basis. Transient populations, probably from the lower Segama and Kuamut Rivers, clearly reached Danum – as evidenced by coffins which can still be seen at sites now occupied by the Borneo Rainforest Lodge and Danum Valley Field Centre – but there is no indication that these nomadic groups either settled for long periods or engaged in shifting cultivation. The forests of central and eastern Sabah remained, until the advent of industrial logging in the latter half of the twentieth century, almost completely untouched.

The search for gold provided the impetus for the first serious attempts to exploit the area for its resources – with both the Segama and Bole Rivers being regularly, albeit mostly abortively, explored from the mid-nineteenth century onwards by the British North Borneo Gold Syndicate. Although alluvial gold was discovered, no substantial outcroppings of gold-containing rocks were ever found and interest eventually faded.

Logging history

The British forester, Harry Keith, appointed as the Conservator of Forests by the British North Borneo Company in the 1930s, conducted the first surveys of the forests surrounding Danum Valley – but it was not until the 1960s that forestry operations commenced in the area with the arrival of the Kennedy Bay Timber Company from America. Through an arrangement with Yayasan Sabah, then newly formed and with management rights over the entire area, a large sawmill was constructed on the coast close to Gunung Silam and industrial logging of the forests of the Ulu Segama Reserve, to the east of what is now the Danum Valley Conservation Area, commenced. Through the 1970s, 1980s and early 1990s the forests surrounding Danum, including the Malua Forest Reserve to the north of Danum, were selectively

A logging road cut through dipterocarp forest. To minimise damage to soils and other vegetation, Sabah now uses Reduced-Impact Logging (RIL) techniques across the entire state.

logged (removing the largest trees of commercial species, mostly dipterocarps) at a rate of approximately 30 sq km annually. These areas comprised some of the richest timber stands in the SE Asian tropics and rates of extraction were extremely high – with, in many cases, high levels of damage done to the residual vegetation as a result of the use of bulldozers, cable yarding machines and other heavy logging machinery. By the mid 1990s the forests surrounding Danum (and those in the vicinity of Maliau Basin and Imbak Canyon, which had generally been managed in a similar way) had been largely exhausted of timber and logging operations ceased. With a recommended harvesting rotation of 60 years, and with the timber mill at Silam having been largely decommissioned, it was assumed that these forests would not be logged again for decades – if at all, given increasing global and local interest in conservation, forest restoration and research (especially following the opening of the Danum Valley Field Centre) and in the role of forests in mitigating climate change.

At this point, at the end of the 1990s, the forests which were to become the 'Green Heart' of Sabah comprised a mosaic of areas degraded by logging, interspersed with less damaged forests,

Rather than clearing land for commercial plantations, such as for oil palm, the connected landscape of the extended conservation corridor will focus on the regeneration of commercially-important tree species within the degraded forest, ensuring higher levels of diversity.

often on steeper slopes which were more difficult or even impossible to log. Both Maliau Basin and Danum Valley had, by this stage, been set aside by Yayasan Sabah as fully protected areas and moves were afoot to conserve Imbak Canyon, which remained untouched.

However, the cessation of logging in these forests was to be short-lived and, catalysed by an agreement between the Malaysian and Chinese Governments to develop a huge pulp mill and associated plantation within the Yayasan Sabah area, logging re-started over extensive areas surrounding Danum Valley in the late 1990s, at least 30 years in advance of the recommended harvesting rotation. As a pre-cursor to eventual conversion of natural forest to exotic timber plantations, the range of species harvested was expanded to include non-dipterocarps, the size of tree permitted for felling was reduced, the speed of logging greatly increased and even heavy-lift helicopters deployed to allow previously un-loggable steep areas and hill tops to be harvested. Forests which had taken decades to harvest on a first-cut basis were re-logged in less than 10 years, leaving extensive areas in a highly degraded condition. Mercifully, plans for the plantations and the pulp mill they would have fed were ultimately abandoned – under intense local and international pressure – and the environmental calamity of the loss of the crucially-important natural forest linkage between Silam, Danum, Imbak and Maliau - the 'Green Heart' of Sabah - was averted. Logging finally ceased in these forests at the end of 2007, although they remained as part of Sabah's commercial forest reserve and hence without protection from future re-logging and at some risk of conversion to plantation.

The intact forests of Sabah's 'Green Heart' provide vital ecosystem-related services for the people of Sabah, including protecting soils and watersheds, and acting as carbon sinks - vital in the face of rising atmospheric CO_2 levels and global warming.

Conservation and restoration

Moves to conserve significant areas of lowland forest in eastern Sabah started with Danum Valley, with the area gaining full protection as a Class I Forest Reserve in 1995. By this stage, Maliau Basin had been voluntarily protected by Yayasan Sabah, and within 10 years both Maliau and Imbak Canyon, the remaining pristine forest conservation areas under the management of Yayasan Sabah, had been fully protected as Class I Forest Reserves. Together, Danum, Maliau and Imbak total almost 1,500 sq km and comprise an altitudinal range of some 1,400 m, covering more than a dozen distinct vegetation types from the lowland dipterocarp-dominated forests of Danum, to the Kerangas and heath forest associations of Maliau Basin. Moreover, and almost uniquely in SE Asia, the forests of Danum, Maliau and Imbak are subject to only minimal hunting pressure, with all of the large mammal and bird species found in the different forest types at near-natural levels of abundance – species which have often been hunted to near exhaustion elsewhere in Borneo.

With the cessation of logging in the forests to the east and north of Danum and between it and Maliau Basin, and with no likelihood of there being a worthwhile volume of timber to harvest for decades, fears grew that the pressure to at least partially convert these forests to agricultural or timber plantations would become irresistible. These concerns were magnified as adjacent areas of natural forest in Sabah, including areas managed by the Yayasan Sabah, were converted – including to oil palm plantations. However, following a series of decisions in 2011 and 2012, the Sabah Forestry Department, with the sanction of the state government, placed the future of this great swathe of forest, which had been subject to logging and threatened with conversion for decades, beyond any doubt. Within the space of just a year, some 3,500 km of forest (in addition to the existing protected areas) – linking Silam in the east with Danum Valley, Imbak Canyon and Maliau Basin to the west – were conserved.

Science and research play important roles within Sabah's conservation areas. Locations such as the Danum Valley offer opportunities for cutting-edge research, the results of which can be applied to the management of other tropical forest areas across the globe.

The protection of Danum Valley - along with the burgeoning collaborative research programme supported by its Field Centre in partnership with the UK's Royal Society - acted as a magnet for a number of pioneering forest restoration, sustainable forest management and conservation projects, and major field-based experimental programmes, which continue to cluster around Danum to this day. Perhaps most notable among these, not least given its strategic location on the eastern flank of the Danum Valley Conservation Area, is the Innoprise-FACE Foundation Rainforest Rehabilitation Project (INFAPRO), one of the largest forest restoration projects in SE Asia and one that pre-dated the Kyoto Protocol on climate change. Innoprise – the operational arm of Yayasan Sabah – entered into an agreement with the Forests Absorbing Carbon Emissions (FACE) Foundation of the Netherlands in 1992 with the aim of restoring a total of 300 sq km of forest through a combination of enrichment planting with dipterocarp seedlings and silvicultural treatment to improve the growth both of planted and naturally regenerating dipterocarps, so as to increase the forest's capacity to sequester carbon dioxide from the atmosphere. In short succession, a major study into the benefits of Reduced Impact Logging (RIL) was instituted which clearly demonstrated that the sustainable management of tropical forests was not only possible, but economically viable (on the basis of broadly equivalent timber yields to 'conventional' logging and reduced time spans between harvesting rotations) and resulted in significantly reduced carbon emissions as compared to standard logging practices. Techniques developed on the INFAPRO and RIL projects have been rolled-out among a suite of forest restoration and management projects, involving both Yayasan Sabah and the Sabah Forestry Department, and are now being included in the guidelines for sustainable management with which all forestry operations in Sabah are required to comply.

Scientists are only now beginning to understand the full magnitude of species diversity within Sabah's forests. In particular, only in recent decades have researchers realised just how important invertebrates such as insects are within the forest ecosystem.

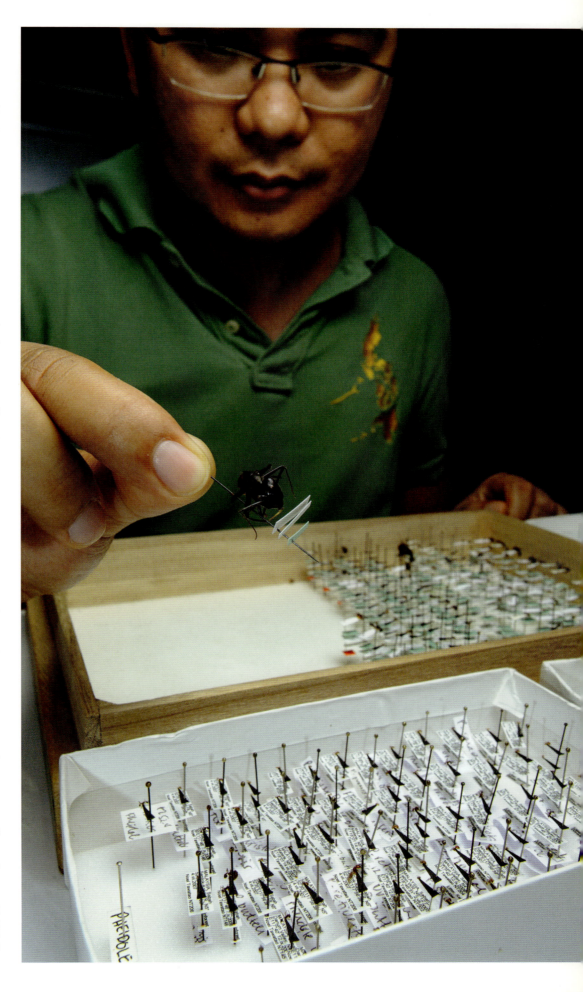

Recently, scientists have discovered that fragments of forest surrounded by commercial plantations are unable to recruit and regenerate commercially-important species such as dipterocarps, underlining the importance of maintaining pristine forests within a mixed-use landscape.

Connectivity, fragmentation and the importance of continuous forest in an era of climate change

One of the key messages to emerge from the now 30+ year research programme at Danum Valley is the extent to which heavily logged, highly degraded rainforest is important in supporting biodiversity; even repeated logging appears not to have the severe impact that might intuitively be assumed. Across a range of taxa, species show considerable resilience to disturbance by selective logging and although rare endemic species inhabiting deep, undisturbed forest, species which occupy the forest canopy and soil dwelling organisms are all likely to be disproportionately impacted by logging, there is little evidence to suggest that any species have gone extinct in Sabah as a direct consequence of selective logging. Some studies now suggest that species assemblages, including the rare endemics, recover in forests restored by enrichment planting – highlighting the importance of maintaining and restoring not just the extent of forest but its quality.

Numerous scientific studies from Sabah and across the tropics clearly show that the fragmentation of natural forest – which is often driven by the expansion of agricultural plantations, particularly oil palm plantations in the Malaysian context – severely impacts biodiversity, resulting in reductions in the abundance of all but the most robust, ubiquitous species and, in many cases, local extinctions. Although many plantations include embedded areas of forest, research shows that the keystone species of the forests of Sabah – trees from the Dipterocarpaceae family – appear

Sabah's vast network of protected areas and managed forests will become a model for conservation in the future - a mixed-use landscape that will put diversity and ecosystem-related services above the wholesale exploitation of the environment.

not to recruit adequately in even very large forest fragments (of several hundred hectares) suggesting that natural forests within plantation landscapes may, over time, degrade to the point at which they no longer persist or even function as forests to any recognisable extent. Although further research into the effects of fragmentation - including the role that forest patches might play in providing 'stepping stones' through plantation-dominated landscapes - is essential, the evidence for the importance of retaining large, continuous areas of natural forest is unequivocal.

The continuous and now fully protected forests of the 'Green Heart' of Sabah assume even greater importance as the influence of climate change, driven by global warming, accelerates across SE Asia. The level of species diversity supported by Danum, Maliau, Imbak and Silam and their surrounding forests, and the extent and range of habitat types represented, confers a degree of robustness – a biological insurance policy - as temperatures warm and weather patterns change. Of even greater significance is that these forests represent an unbroken altitudinal gradient running from sea level to above 1,600 m and, as importantly, a rainfall gradient from the drier, more drought-prone coastal areas, to the much wetter forests of the interior. In order to allow species to shift their range - from the warmer low-lying forests to cooler upland areas - in response to changing temperature and rainfall patterns, it is crucial that continuous forests which include these ecological gradients are fully protected.

The conservation of the forests of the 'Green Heart' of Sabah is of truly global significance. By raising the extent of protected forests to close to a fifth of the state's total land area - including the embedded pristine forests of Danum, Maliau, Imbak and Silam at the core of this connected landscape - Sabah has ensured that critical habitat for many of Borneo's most iconic and threatened species has been secured in perpetuity – even in the face of a changing climate – cementing Sabah's reputation as a regional model for evidence-based conservation and land-use planning.

BEHIND THE LENS

By Jason Isley

Rainforests are hot, humid, damp and dark - perfect conditions for the animals and plants that live there, but not quite so conducive for photographers and their equipment. Combined with the mosquitoes and leeches, sharp, spiny rattans and rain - lots of rain - and the result is an extremely difficult environment to work in and attempt to produce high-quality images. For the photographers that contributed to '*The Green Heart of Sabah*', shooting in the forests was a huge, but incredibly rewarding challenge that required a great deal of planning, perseverance, sweat, blood and a little bit of luck.

Getting into the heart of Sabah can be a mission in itself, as most of the access roads to the main research centres are unsealed and, when wet, can quickly become very treacherous. Our first trip into Imbak Canyon - a short recce to see how long we would need for the main shoot - ended in near-disaster when, after driving for 7 hours, tiredness caught up with the driver and we came off the road and rolled into a ditch, writing off the car in the process. Fortunately everyone was OK and - even more importantly - the camera gear survived. Once at the main camps we would often drive to different look-out towers or locations and whilst the

Christian Loader photographing Imbak Falls, Imbak Canyon.

roads can be difficult, we would often encounter wildlife on these drives, including many Bearded Pigs whilst driving into Maliau Basin and a large herd of Pygmy Elephants at Imbak Canyon - an extremely lucky encounter.

To get to the more remote areas of the forests, however, involved lots of trekking, with lots of heavy camera equipment. At Danum Valley most of the treks were relatively short and easy and we quickly found ourselves adapting to the natural rhythms of the forest. Every day we would head out before dawn in the cool of the early morning, in search of gibbons, orangutans and birds, rest during the midday heat like most of the wildlife, then head out again in the late afternoon. We would also do a lot of night treks in search of tarsiers, frogs and slow loris around the research centre itself. The days at Danum were long, hot and humid but the valley is an incredible location for wildlife and we managed to shoot many of the subjects we hoped to cover during our stay there.

At Imbak Canyon there were plenty of different nature trails and the main waterfall just thirty minutes drive from the base camp - so we had plenty of locations to chose from and we were kept very busy close to the camp. Capturing Kuli Falls was quite a mission however. Christian and Roger made the trek to Kuli Camp and then an arduous ascent up Gunung Kuli - climbing steep ridges covered in dense forest with all the camera equipment - but the views over Imbak Canyon and Kuli Falls made it all worthwhile. Back at Tampoi Camp, myself and Matt concentrated on the forest and wildlife shots - with one particular little frog choosing to be very elusive. I spent five nights in a row trying to shoot a Spotted Stream Frog that had been seen just a short walk from Tampoi Camp, but it took until the sixth night, after some heavy rain, before I finally managed to obtain the shots I wanted.

Our next destination - Maliau Basin - was much more difficult and the trekking became very tough. Our plan was to cover the main sites and diverse forest habitats by trekking and staying at the Nepenthes and Ginseng Camps. The first trek, from Agathis Camp to Nepenthes Camp, involved some steep climbing but fortunately we had several porters with us to help with the equipment. Once at Nepenthes Camp we trekked further into the basin, to Takob-Akob and Giluk Falls. During our time in Maliau Basin we had a great deal of rain which added to the difficulty of shooting, as well as making the climbing much more treacherous - in fact I lost count of the number of times myself and Sam, our cameraman, fell to the floor in the mud.

Sam Lewis starting the arduous trek from Agathis camp to Nepenthes camp, Maliau Basin.

Sam Lewis gaining an interesting vantage point, Danum Valley.

Gil Woolley crossing the canopy walkway at Borneo Rainforest Lodge, Danum Valley.

Sam Lewis filming a Malayan Horned Frog in the mud, Danum Valley.

Jason Isley shooting fungi on elephant dung, Danum Valley.

Ch'ien Lee in a camouflaged hide used to photograph shy birds, Danum Valley.

Capturing high-quality images of birds requires a lot of patience and a touch of luck. Knowing where they like to feed or rest is very important but more often than not, the only way to get the shots would involve sitting and waiting in some form of hide for hours on end. Sitting in one spot in the heat of the forest is not the easiest thing to do - especially with Sabah's abundant mosquitoes and leeches! Leeches are found in all the forests and even with the protection of leech socks, they have an incredible knack of finding their way into your boots, down your shirts and even into your trousers - pretty much everywhere. We encountered the highest number of leeches whilst trekking through Maliau Basin and as soon as you stepped away from the camp, our boots would be covered in half-a-dozen of the little suckers and on a few occasions, we even had them coming up through the timber floors of the camps to 'attack' us. We also encountered a number of wasps around the camps in the Maliau Basin and getting stung on the hand by one of them made handling the camera rather awkward over the following days.

Many of the animals of the forests are considered dangerous - including venomous snakes, scorpions and even cute orangutans - but they are only aggressive if provoked or if they feel threatened. If you show them the respect they deserve you can still get the shots you want. We were fortunate to have guides with a great deal of knowledge and experience with these animals - a huge help, not only for finding our subjects, but also knowing how to approach them. However, even with the best intentions some creatures are simply having a bad day, and one angry large male orangutan took great pleasure urinating on us from high up in a tree!

Our nemesis - a Tiger Leech, Danum Valley.

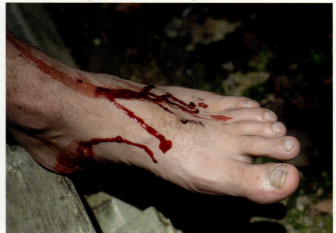

Jason Isley photographing Harlequin Tree Frogs, Danum Valley.

Sam Lewis' foot after feeding the leeches, Maliau Basin.

The harsh conditions within the forest took their toll on the equipment, as well as the photographers. Keeping our cameras dry and in good working order was a daily challenge. Lenses hate the damp, humid air and quite often would mist up, normally just when you're about to capture an award-winning shot! We use Nikon cameras and take a whole range of lenses on all shoots, from macro lenses that are fantastic for capturing the tiny bugs, to one of our favourites, a fisheye lens, which we use to show the small animals of the forest in their natural habitat. But even with all the right equipment, the early morning starts and arduous trekking, many of the images in this book came down to luck - being in the right place at the right time. And often-as-not we were simply in the wrong place at the wrong time - it was amazing how many times we heard 'you should have been here yesterday'… Such is life as a photographer in the forests of 'The Green Heart of Sabah'.

ACKNOWLEDGMENTS

Scubazoo has called Sabah its home for the last 17 years and during that time we have been fortunate enough to make many loyal friends, including the author, Wendy Hutton. We have worked with Wendy on a number of projects in the past and when she approached Scubazoo with the idea of publishing a large-format coffee table book about Sabah's amazing forests, we jumped at the chance. We are forever grateful that you came to us with this incredible idea and for your inspiration and knowledge.

We would like to express our gratitude to the Chief Minister of Sabah, Datuk Seri Panglima Musa Haji Aman, for his continued support of Scubazoo throughout our time in Sabah.

We are indebted to Datuk Sam Mannan and Fred Kugan, and the Sabah Forestry Department as a whole, for their sponsorship of *The Green Heart of Sabah*, as well as your faith in Scubazoo to complete this publication in time for the Department's anniversary celebrations - many congratulations on 100 years of the Sabah Forestry Department!

We would like to thank Mr George Hong, General Manager of the wonderful Borneo Rainforest Lodge, Salehuddin Jais for his assistance and all the staff at BRL for their kind hospitality. We also thank Serena Loy from Borneo Nature Tours for her help.

The images within this book were produced over the course of several photographic trips and these would not have been possible without the support of Yayasan Sabah - many thanks to Dr Waidi Sinun for your support and Jenifer Chua Sin Yee for your kind assistance and information. During each of the trips to Maliau Basin, Danum Valley and Imbak Canyon we were assisted by the amazing nature guides in these conservation areas, who helped us to find elusive creatures and made the arduous treks with the huge amounts of camera equipment a little easier.

We would also like to acknowledge the assistance of Vivian Rudolf from the Sabah Forestry Department for his help with our visits to Gunung Silam.

Lastly, Scubazoo would like to take this opportunity to thank Dr Glen Reynolds of SEARRP for his contributions to this project, as well as his continued support over the years.

SABAH FORESTRY DEPARTMENT

YAYASAN SABAH

SEARRP South East Asia Rainforest Research Programme

PHOTOGRAPHY CREDITS

Jason Isley has lived in Sabah since 1996, when he helped to create Scubazoo Sdn Bhd. An experienced cameraman and photographer, he has filmed and photographed extensively all over the world. Focusing on his passion for photography and design, Jason is the driving force behind Scubazoo Publications.

Biologist turned photographer, **Ch'ien Lee** has worked in California as an environmental educator prior to moving to Borneo in 1996. He has worked as a full time freelance wildlife photographer and consultant since 2003 and now travels widely across Southeast Asia to document the region's astounding biodiversity through imagery.

Christian Loader joined the Scubazoo team in 2007. After long-term assignments in the Maldives and Indonesia, he turned his attention to photography, and with passion and creativity he has won many international awards for his images.

Matthew Oldfield is a freelance photographer and writer based in Bali, Indonesia. Trained as a biologist, he worked as an underwater photographer and location manager with Scubazoo before going freelance in 2007. Today his work includes event, music and natural history photography, as well as photojournalism.

Gilbert Woolley, Scubazoo photographer and project manager, has been involved with natural history imagery for the past 17 years as an editor, creative director and photographer. He has worked on countless books during this time and has combined his scientific background with creative photography and design.

Key: T-Top, B-Bottom, M-Middle, L-Left, R-Right.

Jason Isley: Front cover(L)(M), inside front cover, 6(T)(M)(MB)(B), 7(T)(M)(MB), 8-9, 12-13, 16(B), 19(B), 20, 21, 32-33, 34, 35(T)(B), 36, 37(L)(R), 39, 40-41, 42(T), 43, 45, 46(B)(T), 58(B), 60-61, 69(L), 78-79, 80(T), 81, 82-83, 84(L)(R), 85, 86-87, 89(T)(B), 90, 97(B), 99, 101, 105(M), 106(T)(B), 108(TR)(BL), 109(TL)(TM)(TR)(B), 112, 113(TL)(B), 116(TL)(TR), 117(T), 118-119, 120(T)(BL), 123(T)(B), 126(M), 127(B), 128-129, 130(TL), 138-139, 140(B), 141(TL)(TR), 145(T), 146(T), 150, 151(BR), 152(L)(R), 154-155, 158-159, 160(T), 161(T)(B), 162, 163(T)(BL), 164, 165, 166(T), 170, 172, 173(T), 175(B), 176-177, 178, 179, 182(B), 183, 185(T), 188(T), 189(R), 195, 196(B), 202-203, 204, 205(T), 208, 210(T), 211(T)(B), 218-219, 222-223, 224(T), 231(T)(B), 238-239, 240, 241(T)(MB), 243(BR), 246(M), 247(M)(R), 248(L)(M), 249(L)(R), 256, inside back cover, back cover.

Ch'ien C. Lee: 2-3, 7(B), 22-23, 38, 56-57, 64-65, 67, 70, 96, 97(T), 98(B), 100(T), 102, 103(T)(B), 104(T)(BL)(BR), 113(TR), 116(B), 120(BR), 121(T)(B), 124-125, 127(M), 130(TM)(TR)(BL)(BR), 131(TL)(BL), 134(BL), 136, 142-143, 146(B), 147(B), 149(B), 151(TL)(TR), 153(T)(B), 157(B), 167, 168-169, 171, 173(B), 175(T), 180(T)(B), 181(B), 182(T), 186-187, 188(BR), 189(L), 190(TL)(TR)(ML)(BL), 191(B), 192(T)(B), 193, 194, 198-199, 207(TR), 214-215, 220(T)(B), 221(T)(B), 228-229, 232-233, 234(T)(BL)(BR), 235.

Christian Loader: 1, 4-5, 6(MT), 7(MT), 25(T), 30(T), 48-49, 50, 51(T)(B), 52(T)(B), 53, 54-55, 55(B), 58-59, 62(L), 72(T), 74(L), 75(TR), 88, 92-93, 100(B), 105(L), 108(TL)(BR), 110-111, 114-115, 117(BL)(BR), 122(T)(B), 126(B), 131(BR), 132, 133, 135, 140(T), 141(B), 144(T), 145(B), 147(T), 148(T)(B), 149(T), 151(M), 156, 157(T), 160(B), 163(BR), 174, 181(T), 184(T)(B), 185(B), 196(T), 197(T)(B), 205(B), 206(T), 207(TL), 209, 212, 217, 224(BL), 225, 230(L), 237, 241(MT), 243(L)(TR), 247(L), 250-251.

Matt Oldfield: 16(R), 17, 18, 24(R), 25(B), 26(T), 31(T), 47, 59(B), 68, 69(TR)(BR), 71, 72(B), 73(T)(B), 75(TL), 76(T)(B), 77, 80(B), 91, 94(T)(B), 95(TL)(TR)(BL)(BR), 98(TR), 105(R), 107, 151(BL), 241(B), 246(L)(R), 248(R), 249(M).

Gil Woolley: Front cover(R), 14, 24(L), 26(B), 27, 28-29, 30(B), 31(B), 63, 66, 74(R), 75(B), 98(BR), 126(T), 127(T), 131(TR), 134(T), 137, 144(B), 166(B), 188(BL), 190(BR), 191(T), 200, 201(T)(BL)(BR), 206(B), 207(BL)(BM)(BR), 216, 246(L), 248(R).

Additional photography:

Bob Hartley/Dragonfly Robotix: 42(B), 44.
Simon Enderby: 213, 226, 227.
Roger Munns: 19(T), 210(B).

SPONSORS

SABAH FORESTRY DEPARTMENT

Locked Bag 68,
90009 Sandakan, Malaysia
TEL: +60 89 242 500

www.forest.sabah.gov.my

Yayasan Sabah Headquaters
Menara Tun Mustapha, Teluk Likas
P. O. BOX 11201, 88813 Kota Kinabalu, Sabah
TEL: +60 88 326 300

www.ysnet.org.my

SPONSORS

FOCUS LUMBER BHD

JAYAKUIK SDN. BHD

TAWAU GREEN ENERGY SDN. BHD

HAP SENG CONSOLIDATED BERHAD

CYMAO HOLDINGS BERHAD

SAPULUT FOREST DEVELOPMENT SDN. BHD.

MAXLAND BERHAD

HORMAT JADI SDN. BHD.
SATRIA ERAMAJU SDN. BHD.
MULIA ERAMAJU SDN. BHD.
LEBIHASIL SDN. BHD.
KTS PLANTATION SEDN. BHD.
EMPARYAR KEJORA SDN. BHD.
BORNION TIMBER SDN. BHD.
ANIKA DESIRAN SDN. BHD.

Borneo Rainforest Lodge
Danum Valley

Borneo Nature Tours an inbound tour operator specializing in nature, adventure tour programmes in Sabah and the marketing agent for the award-winning BORNEO RAINFOREST LODGE

www.borneonaturetours.com

Block D, Ground Floor, Lot 10
Sadong Jaya Complex
P.O.Box 11622
88100 Kota Kinabalu
Sabah, Malaysia

Tel: +60 88 267637
Fax: +60 88 251636
Email: info@borneonaturetours.com

INDEX

A

Acrophylla titan, 148
Agathis forest, Imbak Canyon, 43
Agathis forest, Maliau Basin, 37
Ahaetulla prasina, 180
Amolops sp., 39
Anomala sp., 120
Anorrhinus galeritus, 194
Ant plant, Gunung Silam, 147
Ant plant, Maliau Basin, 37
Anthracoceros albirostris, 195
Anthracoceros malayanus, 197
Ants, 146-147
Aphaniotis ornata, 170
Apis dorsata, 69
Arachnothera longirostra, 100
Arctogalidia trivirgata, 54
Argus Pheasant, Danum Valley, 198-199
Argusianus argus, 198-199
Asian Army Ants, Danum Valley, 147
Asian Fairy-bluebird, Danum Valley, 190
Asian Forest Tortoise, Imbak Canyon, 184
Asian Paradise-Flycatcher, Danum Valley, 190
Assassin bug, Danum Valley, 137
Assassin bug, feeding, Danum Valley, 157

B

Bantengs, Maliau Basin, 38
Bark, 94
Batocera lineolata, 123
Batocera rufomaculata, 122
Bats, as seed dispersers, 18
Batu Timbang, Imbak Canyon, 44
Bay Cat, Danum Valley, 29
Bearded Pig, Danum Valley, 212
Bearded Pigs, Maliau Basin, 38
Beccari's Keeled Skink, Imbak Canyon, 175
Beetles, diversity of, 30, 69, 119
Begonia postarii Kiew, 44
Begonia, Danum Valley, 98
Begonia, Imbak Canyon, 44
Behind the Scenes, 239-243
Belian, Imbak Canyon, 43
Belian, Maliau Basin, 36
Bird's Nest Fern, Danum Valley, 229
Bird's Nest Fern, Imbak Canyon, 69
Birds, 186-199
Birdwing Butterfly caterpillar, Maliau Basin, 144
Black Hornbill, Imbak Canyon, 197
Black-and-crimson Pitta, Danum Valley, 193
Black-and-red Broadbill, Danum Valley, 188
Black-and-yellow Broadbill, Danum Valley, 188
Black-headed Cat Snake, Danum Valley, 180
Black-spotted Rock Frog, Danum Valley, 166
Blackwater streams, 18
Blackwater streams, Maliau Basin, 37, 80
Blue-headed Pitta, Danum Valley, 192
Blue-throated Bee-eater, Danum Valley, 189
Boiga nigriceps, 180
Bornean Angle-headed Lizard, Danum Valley, 31, 173
Bornean Angle-headed Lizard, Imbak Canyon, 172
Bornean Banded Pitta, Danum Valley, 192

Bornean Bristlehead, Danum Valley, 186-187, 29
Bornean Orangutans, 19
Bornean Orangutans, conservation, 209
Bornean Orangutans, Danum Valley, 208, 209, 210, 211
Bornean Orangutans, population in Danum Valley, 27
Bornean Orangutans, population in Maliau Basin, 38
Bornean Orangutans, speciation, 27
Bornean Pit Viper, Danum Valley, 179
Bornean Pygmy Elephants, 8-9, 222-225
Bornean Pygmy Elephants, conservation, 46, 235
Bornean Pygmy Elephants, evolution, 235
Bornean Pygmy Elephants, Imbak Canyon, 222-223, 45, 46, 234, 235
Bornean Pygmy Elephants, speciation, 46
Bornean Tree-hole Frog, Danum Valley, 163
Borneo Falconet, Danum Valley, 201
Borneo Keeled Pit Viper, 178
Borneo Rainforest Lodge, 24
Borneo Rainforest Lodge, canopy walkway, 28
Borneo, diversity of animals, 14
Borneo, diversity of fungi, 14
Borneo, diversity of plants, 13
Borneo, isolation during ice age, 14
Bos javanicus, 38
Broadbills, 188
Brown Wood Owl, Danum Valley, 201
Bubo ketupu, 200
Buceros rhinoceros, 196
Buceros vigil, 196
Buffy Fish Owl, Danum Valley, 200
Bulbophyllum patens, 109
Burial site, Danum Valley, 24, 230
Bushy-crested Hornbill, Danum Valley, 194
Butterflies, 140
Buttress roots, 17, 72

C

Calanthe zollingeri, 108
Callophyllium sakarium, 51
Callosciurus notatus, 51
Calomera crespignyi, 121
Camera trap images, 220
Camouflage, 130-131, 160-162
Canopy gaps, 16
Carnivores, 220-221
Casuarina-Conifer forest, Maliau Basin, 37
Caterpillars, defences, 145
Cephalopachus bancanus borneanus, 217
Ceriscoides imbakensis, 43
Chaerilus solegladi, 153
Chalcosoma mollenkampi, 118-119
Charaxes affinis, 140
Chestnut-rumped Babbler, Danum Valley, 191
Chorotypus gallinaceus, 131
Cicada, emerging as adult, 135
Clavicipitaceae fungus, 116
Click Beetle, Imbak Canyon, 46
Climbers, 73
Climbing plants, Danum Valley, 69
Collett's Tree Frog, Danum Valley, 161
Collett's Tree Frog, Imbak Canyon, 46
Colugo, Danum Valley, 216
Commercial logging, 230, 231

Common Mock Viper, Gunung Silam, 181
Conservation corridor, common management strategy, 21
Conservation corridor, connected landscape, 21
Corybas serpentius, 52
Corydon sumatranus, 188
Cosmolestes picticeps, 137
Creobroter gemmatus, 127
Crested Serpent Eagle, Danum Valley, 201
Crimson Marsh Glider, 4-5
Culicicapa ceylonensis, 190
Cup Moth caterpillar, Danum Valley, 145
Cylindera versicolor, 121
Cymbidium finlaysonianum, 109
Cymbirhynchus macrorhynchos, 188
Cynocephalus variegatus, 216
Cynotrachelus flavotuberosus, 124-125
Cyriopalus wallacei, 123
Cyrtodactylus consobrinus, 174

D

Danum Valley Conservation Area, 23-31, 12
Danum Valley Conservation Area, 'big five' animals, 27
Danum Valley Conservation Area, amphibian species, 29
Danum Valley Conservation Area, bird species, 29
Danum Valley Conservation Area, burial site, 24, 30, 230
Danum Valley Conservation Area, canopy, 26
Danum Valley Conservation Area, conservation, 24-25, 30
Danum Valley Conservation Area, diversity of animals, 27
Danum Valley Conservation Area, diversity of invertebrates, 30
Danum Valley Conservation Area, diversity of plants, 26
Danum Valley Conservation Area, early history, 24
Danum Valley Conservation Area, human habitation, 24
Danum Valley Conservation Area, mammal species, 28
Danum Valley Conservation Area, observation platforms, 24
Danum Valley Conservation Area, partnership with Royal Society, 25
Danum Valley Conservation Area, protection of, 25
Danum Valley Conservation Area, range of altitudes, 23
Danum Valley Conservation Area, reptile species, 29
Danum Valley Conservation Area, research programme, 31
Danum Valley Conservation Area, size, 23
Danum Valley Research Centre, aerial, 22
Danum Valley Research Centre, facilities, 24
Danum Valley Research Centre, suspension bridge, 25
Danum Valley, canopy, 62
Danum Valley, mists, 60-61
Danum Valley, sunrise, 21
Darvel Bay, from Gunung Silam, 48-49
Dead Leaf Grasshopper, Danum Valley, 131
Dead Leaf Mantis, Danum Valley, 128-129
Degredation of forests, 21
Dendrelaphis formosus, 181
Dendrobium cinnabarinum, 108
Dendrobium jamirusii, 44
Dendrobium metachilinum, 109

Deroplatys desiccata, 128-129
Dicerorhinus sumatrensis, 226-227
Dipteris lobbiana, 82-83
Dipterocarp forests, 17
Dipterocarp forests, canopy, 17
Dipterocarp forests, commercial importance, 20, 30
Dipterocarp forests, Danum Valley, 25, 62, 63, 66, 67
Dipterocarp forests, flowering, 96, 97, 103
Dipterocarp forests, Gunung Silam, 50
Dipterocarp forests, Imbak Canyon, 43, 44, 47
Dipterocarp forests, layers, 62
Dipterocarp forests, lowland, Imbak Canyon, 43
Dipterocarp forests, Maliau Basin, 36
Dipterocarp forests, species composition, 17, 36
Dipterocarp forests, species richness, 26
Dipterocarp forests, structure, 62
Dipterocarps, new species, 43
Dipterocarps, pollination by thrips, 18
Dipterocarps, seeds, 104
Dipterocarpus megacarpus, 43
Dogania subplana, 185
Domatia, Gunung Silam, 147
Draco cornutus, 168-169, 171
Draco Lizard, Danum Valley, 168-169, 171
Durian, Danum Valley, 105
Dusky Broadbill, Danum Valley, 188
Dysmorpha obesa, 132

E

Ecosystems, 14, 18
Ecotones, 37
Elephas maximus borneensis, 8-9, 45, 222-225, 234, 235
Emergents, 17
Emergents, Danum Valley, 26, 64-65
Emergents, Imbak Canyon, 43
Endemism, Gunung Silam, 51
Endemism, Imbak Canyon, 43
Epeus sp., 151
Epiphytes, Danum Valley, 14, 26
Epiphytes, diversity of, 17, 69
Ethnobotanical remedies, 44
Eurylaimus ochromalus, 188

F

Ferns, Danum Valley, 68
Ferns, Imbak Canyon, 71, 82-83
Field research, 234
Fig, fruiting, 105
Fight for Light, 16, 35
Figs, Danum Valley, 26
Figs, keystone species, 17
Figs, pollination by wasps, 18
File-eared Tree Frog, Imbak Canyon, 164
Fish life, Danum Valley, 92-93
Flooding, 84
Flying Lemur, Danum Valley, 216
Forest canopy, Imbak Canyon, 43
Forest Management, 229-237
Forests, conservation, 230
Forests, development of different types, 35
Forests, different types, 17

Forests, ecosystem services, 19
Forests, ecotones, 37
Forests, fragmentation of, 21, 236
Forests, layers of, 26
Forests, microhabitats in canopy, 69
Forests, physical conditions, 14
Forests, role as carbon sinks, 20
Forests, role in flood prevention, 20
Forests, role in protecting soils, 20
Forests, structure of, 16
Forests, understory of, 26
Frilled Tree Frog, Danum Valley, 160, 162
Frogs, 158-167
Frogs, camouflage, 160-162, 165
Frogs, diversity of, 29, 162
Frogs, foot flagging behaviour, 39
Frogs, life cycles, 166-167
Frogs, Maliau Basin, 39
Frogs, tadpoles, 167
Fruit species, wild relatives, 26, 36
Fungi, 116-117
Fungi, bioluminescent, 117
Fungi, Danum Valley, 19
Fungi, growing on elephant dung, 117

G

Gasteracantha sp., 151
Geesinkorchis altaticallosa, 109
Geosesarma aurantium, 55
Giant Bee, Danum Valley, 69
Giant Leaf Katydid, Danum Valley, 131
Giant Pill Millipede, Danum Valley, 152
Giluk Falls, Maliau Basin, 89
Gingers, Imbak Canyon, 44
Gingers, Maliau Basin, 98
Ginseng Falls, Maliau Basin, 89
Giraffe Weevil, Danum Valley, 124-125
Gliding animals, 170
Gliding animals, frogs, 158-159, 160
Gliding animals, lizards, 168-169
Glomeris sp., 152
Golden Forest Ant, Danum Valley, 146
Golden Orb-weaver Spider, 154-155
Gonocephalus borneensis, 31, 172, 173
Grammatophyllum speciosum, 107
Gray's Malayan Stick Insect, Danum Valley, 148
Green Chafer Beetle, Imbak Canyon, 120
Green Mantis, 16
Green Mantis, Danum Valley, 156
Grey-headed Canary Flycatcher, Danum Valley, 190
Gunung Kuli, Imbak Canyon, 1, 42
Gunung Lotung, Maliau Basin, 34
Gunung Silam, 49-54
Gunung Silam, altitude, 49
Gunung Silam, altitudinal telescoping, 50
Gunung Silam, bird species, 54
Gunung Silam, conservation, 54
Gunung Silam, crab, 54
Gunung Silam, dipterocarp forest, 50
Gunung Silam, diversity of animals, 52
Gunung Silam, diversity of plants, 50
Gunung Silam, endemics, 51
Gunung Silam, endemisim, 51

Gunung Silam, facilities, 49
Gunung Silam, history, 49
Gunung Silam, jewel orchids, 52
Gunung Silam, mammal species, 54
Gunung Silam, Messenerhebung Effect, 50
Gunung Silam, montane forest, 50
Gunung Silam, new species, 52
Gunung Silam, protection of, 49
Gunung Silam, soils, 50
Gunung Silam, sunset, 54-55
Gunung Silam, ultramafic soils, 50

H

Haaniella echinata, 149
Harlequin Tree Frog, Danum Valley, 158-159, 160
Harpactes duvaucelii, 30
Harpactes kasumba, 191
Hawk Moth, Gunung Silam, 141
Hawk Moth, Imbak Canyon, 141
Heath forest, 17, 76-77
Heath forest, density of trees, 17
Heath forest, Gunung Silam, 52
Heath forest, Imbak Canyon, 17, 43
Heath forest, Maliau Basin, 37, 78-79
Heath forest, soils, 17, 18, 37
Heath forest, species composition, 17, 37, 43
Heirodula sp., 16
Helicoptor seeds, 104
Helmeted Hornbill, Danum Valley, 196
Hemiprocne comata, 190
Herpestes brachyurus, 221
Heteropoda boiei, 131, 150
Heteropoda sp., 157
Hierodula sp., 156
Hornbills, 194-197
Hornbills, Imbak Canyon, 46
Hornbills, role as seed dispersers, 46, 196
Hospitalitermes hospitalis, 146
Huntsman Spider, Danum Valley, 157
Hydnophytum sp., 147
Hylarana picturata, 163
Hylobates muelleri, 28, 206
Hymenopus coronatus, 30, 126

I

Imbak Canyon Conservation Area, 41-47, 58-59
Imbak Canyon Conservation Area, amphibian species, 47
Imbak Canyon Conservation Area, Bornean Pygmy Elephants, 46
Imbak Canyon Conservation Area, carnivores, 45
Imbak Canyon Conservation Area, conservation, 47
Imbak Canyon Conservation Area, dipterocarp forest, 43
Imbak Canyon Conservation Area, diversity of animals, 45
Imbak Canyon Conservation Area, diversity of birds, 46
Imbak Canyon Conservation Area, diversity of invertebrates, 47
Imbak Canyon Conservation Area, diversity of plants, 43, 44
Imbak Canyon Conservation Area, emergents, 43

Imbak Canyon Conservation Area, endemisim, 43
Imbak Canyon Conservation Area, exploration of, 42
Imbak Canyon Conservation Area, facilities, 42
Imbak Canyon Conservation Area, geology, 41
Imbak Canyon Conservation Area, gingers, 44
Imbak Canyon Conservation Area, heath forest, 43
Imbak Canyon Conservation Area, mammal species, 45
Imbak Canyon Conservation Area, orchids, 44
Imbak Canyon Conservation Area, protection of, 42
Imbak Canyon Conservation Area,
    range of altitudes, 42
Imbak Canyon Conservation Area, reptile species, 47
Imbak Canyon Conservation Area, size, 41
Imbak Canyon Conservation Area, waterfalls, 42
Imbak Canyon Study Centre, 47
Imbak Canyon, escarpments, 59
Imbak Falls, Imbak Canyon, 40, 42, 86-87, 238-239
Indian Flower Mantis, Danum Valley, 127
INFAPRO, 235
Inocybe sp., 116
Insect diversity, 235
Invertebrates, 118-157
Irena puella, 190

J

Javaen Barb, 92-93
Jewel orchids, Gunung Silam, 52
Jumping Spider, Danum Valley, 151
Juvenile Blue-necked Water Snake, Danum Valley, 182
Juvenile Elegant Bronzeback Snake, Maliau Basin, 181

K

Kacip Fatimah, 44
Kalophrynus sp., 39
Katydid, close-up, 132-133
Katydid, Danum Valley, 130-133
Kenopia striata, 190
Kerangas forest, Maliau Basin, 37
King Cobra, Danum Valley, 29
Koompassia excelsa, 16, 17, 64-65, 68
Kuli Falls, Imbak Canyon, 88
Kurixalus appendiculatus, 160, 162

L

Lake Linumunsut, 35
Lantern bugs, Danum Valley, 134
Leaf Insect, Danum Valley, 130
Leaf Katydid, Danum Valley, 130
Leaf-footed bugs, Danum Valley, 136
Leaf-nosed Pit Viper, Danum Valley, 179
Leafhopper, Danum Valley, 130
Lebeda cognata, 130
Legumes, 17
Lepidiota stigma, 120
Leptobrachium abbot, 163
Leptogenys sp., 147
Lianas, 16, 74
Lichen Huntsman Spider, Danum Valley, 131, 150
Light, availability in the forest, 16, 70
Limnonectes finchi, 167
Little Spiderhunter, Danum Valley, 100
Logging History, 230

Lonchodes brevipes, 148
Long-tailed Macaque, Danum Valley, 204, 205
Long-tongued Nectar Bat, Danum Valley, 102
Longhorn Beetles, 122-123
Lowland Litter Frog, Danum Valley, 163
Lyssa zampa, 138-139

M

Macaca fascicularis, 204, 205
Macaca nemestrina, 205
Macroglossus minimus, 102
Macropisthodon rhodomelas, 182
Majangella moultoni, 126
Malay Civet, Maliau Basin, 39, 218-219
Malay Stink-badger, Danum Valley, 214-215
Malayan Flat-shelled Turtle, Maliau Basin, 184
Malayan Horned Frog, Danum Valley, 30, 165
Malayan Soft-shelled Turtle, Imbak Canyon, 185
Malayan Sun Bear, conservation status, 27
Malayan Sun Bear, Danum Valley, 27
Male Whiskered Treeswift, Danum Valley, 190
Maliau Basin Conservation Area, 33-39
Maliau Basin Conservation Area, amphibian species, 39
Maliau Basin Conservation Area,
    Banteng population, 38
Maliau Basin Conservation Area, bird species, 39
Maliau Basin Conservation Area, canopy, 36
Maliau Basin Conservation Area, coal deposits, 39
Maliau Basin Conservation Area, dipterocarp forest, 36
Maliau Basin Conservation Area, discovery by pilot, 34
Maliau Basin Conservation Area,
    diversity of animals, 38
Maliau Basin Conservation Area,
    diversity of invertebrates, 39
Maliau Basin Conservation Area, diversity of orchids, 37
Maliau Basin Conservation Area,
    diversity of rhododendrons, 37
Maliau Basin Conservation Area, early history, 34
Maliau Basin Conservation Area, ecotones, 37
Maliau Basin Conservation Area, escarpments, 34
Maliau Basin Conservation Area, exploration of, 34
Maliau Basin Conservation Area, facilities, 35
Maliau Basin Conservation Area, geology, 33
Maliau Basin Conservation Area, heath forest, 37
Maliau Basin Conservation Area, Jalan Babi, 38
Maliau Basin Conservation Area,
    mammal species, 38-39
Maliau Basin Conservation Area, Nepenthes Camp, 35
Maliau Basin Conservation Area, protection of, 35
Maliau Basin Conservation Area,
    range of altitudes, 34, 36
Maliau Basin Conservation Area, size, 35
Maliau Basin Conservation Area, Sky Bridge, 35
Maliau Basin Conservation Area, water catchment, 34
Maliau Basin Conservation Area, waterfalls, 34
Maliau Basin Study Centre, aerial, 33
Maliau Basin, rim, 58
Maliau Falls, Maliau Basin, 20, 36, 56-57, 81
Maliau River, 36
Mammals, 202-227
Manouria emys, 184
Mantis, feeding, 156
Mantis, Orchid, Danum Valley, 30
Mantises, 126-129

Marbled Cat, Danum Valley, 220
Maroon Langur, Danum Valley, 27, 202-203, 207
Masked Palm Civet, Danum Valley, 220
Mast fruiting, 96-97
Megophrys nasuta, 30, 165
Mengaris, 16, 17
Mengaris, Danum Valley, 64-65, 68
Mengaris, Maliau Basin, 36
Merops viridis, 189
Messenerhebung Effect, 50
Metaphrynella sundana, 163
Microhierax latifrons, 201
Millipedes, 152
Millipedes, defences, 152
Montane forest, 17
Montane forest, altitude, 17
Montane forest, Gunung Silam, 50, 52
Montane forest, Imbak Canyon, 43
Montane forest, Maliau Basin, 36
Montane forest, species composition, 17, 36
Mormolyce castelnaudi, 120
Moss Mantis, Danum Valley, 126
Moth, camouflaged, 141
Moth, eyes, 141
Moths, 141
Müller's Bornean Gibbon, Danum Valley, 28, 206
Mycena illuminans, 117
Mydaus javanensis, 214-215

N

Neofelis diardi, 45, 221
Nepenthes frog, Maliau Basin, 39
Nepenthes hirsuta, 18
Nepenthes macrovulgaris, 52, 53
Nepenthes reinwardtiana, 37, 113
Nepenthes stenophylla, 113
Nepenthes tentaculata, 110-111
Nepenthes veitchii, 112
Nephila pilipes, 154-155
Notochelys platynota, 184
Nutrient cycle, 19
Nyctyornis amictus, 189

O

Oil Palm Plantations, 236, 237
Olcinia sp., 131
Ophiophagus hannah, 29
Orchid Mantis, Imbak Canyon, 126
Orchids, 108-109
Orchids, diversity, 107
Orchids, Imbak Canyon, 44
Orchids, Maliau Basin, 37
Oriental Pied Hornbill, Danum Valley, 195
Oriental Vine Snake, Danum Valley, 180
Ornate Earless Agama Lizard, 170

P

Paguma larvata, 220
Paratoxodera sp., 127
Pardofelis marmorata, 220
Parias sumatranus, 177
Peter's Forest Gecko, Imbak Canyon, 174
Petronas, partnership at

Imbak Canyon, 47
Phenacephorus sepilokensis, 149
Phormingochilus sp., 151
Phyllium pulchrifolium, 130
Pig-tailed Macaque, Gunung Silam, 205
Pit vipers, 176-179
Pitcher plants, Gunung Silam, 52, 53, 110-111
Pitcher plants, 18, 112-115
Pitcher plants, growing in heath forest, 37
Pitcher plants, Imbak Canyon, 43
Pitcher plants, Maliau Basin, 37, 112
Pitcher plants, viscoelastic biopolymer, 18
Pitta baudii, 192
Pitta schwaneri, 192
Pitta usheri, 193
Pittas, 192-193
Pityriasis gymnocephala, 29, 186-187
Plantain Squirrel, Gunung Silam, 51
Plocoglottis acuminata, 108
Pollination, 100-103
Pollinators, 18
Polypedates colletti, 46, 161
Polypedates otilophus, 164
Polyrhachis ypsilon, 146
Pongo pygmaeus morio, 19, 208, 209, 210, 211
Porbax borneensis, 52
Predatation, 154-157
Presbytis rubicunda, 27, 202-203, 207
Primates, 202-211
Prionochilus maculatus, 100
Psammodynastes pulverulentus, 181
Puntius orphoides, 92-93
Pyrops tranversolineatus, 134
Pyrops whiteheadi, 134
Python reticulatus, 29, 183

R

Rafflesia, 36
Rafflesia tengku-adlinii, 36, 99
Rajah Brooke's Birdwing, 47
Rambutan, Imbak Canyon, 105
Raptors, 201
Red Leaf Monkey, Danum Valley, 27, 202-203, 207
Red-bearded Bee-eater, Danum Valley, 189
Red-naped Trogon, Danum Valley, 191
Red-sided Keelback Snake, Danum Valley, 182
Reduced Imapct Logging, 235
Reptiles, 169-185
Reticulated Python, Danum Valley, 29, 183
Rhacophorous nigropalmatus, 2-3, 30
Rhacophorus pardalis, 158-159, 160
Rheithrosciurus macrotis, 39
Rhinoceros Hornbill, Imbak Canyon, 196
Rhododendron javanica, 106
Rhododendron javanicum subsp. *cladotrichum*, 52
Rhododendron longiflorum var. *subcordatum*, 106
Rhododendron, Gunung Silam, 52
Rhododendrons, 106
Rhomboptera honorabilis, 131
Rhyticeros undulatus, 197
Rock Skipper Frog, Danum Valley, 161
Rough Guardian Frog, Danum Valley, 167
Rough-necked Monitor Lizard, Danum Valley, 175
Rusa unicolor, 213

S

Sabah Forestry Department, forest management, 21
Sabah Forestry Department, history of, 20
Sabah, diversity of animals, 18
Sabah, map, 15
Sabah, percantage of land under protection, 20
Sambar Deer, Danum Valley, 213
Sapagaya Forest Reserve, 49
Saturn Butterfly, Danum Valley, 140
Scarlet-rumped Trogon, Danum Valley, 30
Science and Research, 229-237
Scorpions, 153
Seed dispersal, 18, 102-103, 104-105
Segama River, aerial, 22
Sepilok Stick Insect, Danum Valley, 149
Short-tailed Mongoose, Danum Valley, 221
Slug Moth caterpillar, Danum Valley, 142-143
Snakes, 176-183
Spathoglottis microchilina, 108
Speciation, 14
Spider, feeding, 157
Spiders, 150-151
Spiky Stick Mantis, Danum Valley, 126
Spilornis cheela, 201
Spiny Orb-weaver Spider, Danum Valley, 151
Spiny Stick Insect, Danum Valley, 149
Spotted Stream Frog, Imbak Canyon, 163
Stachyris maculata, 191
Staurois guttatus, 166
Staurois latopalmatus, 161
Stick insects, 148-149
Stick Mantis, Danum Valley, 127
Strangler figs, 75
Streams, Maliau Basin, 38
Striped Wren-babbler, Danum Valley, 190
Strix leptogrammicus, 201
Stunted forest, Maliau Basin, 37
Sumatran Pit Viper, Danum Valley, 177
Sumatran Rhino, breeding programme, 27
Sumatran Rhino, conservation, 227
Sumatran Rhino, Danum Valley, 27
Sumatran Rhino, Tabin Wildlife Reserve, 226-227
Sunda Clouded Leopard, Danum Valley, 221
Sunda Clouded Leopard, Imbak Canyon, 45
Sungai Imbak, Imbak Canyon, 42, 80, 91
Sungai Segama, Danum Valley, 84, 90
Sus barbatus, 38, 212
Syzygium silamense, 51

T

Takob-Akob Falls, Maliau Basin, 85
Tampoi Research Centre, Imbak Canyon, 42
Tampoi Research Centre, Imbak Canyon, aerial, 42
Tarantula, Danum Valley, 151
Tarantula, lifecycle, 151
Temnophyllus sp., 130
Termites, 146
Termites, diversity of, 19
Termites, role in nutrient cycle, 19
Terpsiphone paradisi, 190
Terrestrial crab, Gunung Silam, 55
Theopompa burmeisteri, 127

Three-horned Rhinoceros Beetle, Danum Valley, 118-119
Tiger Beetle, Danum Valley, 121, 157
Tiger Beetles, mating, 121
Titan Stick Insect, Danum Valley, 148
Tongkat Ali, 44
Tower of Heaven, Gunung Silam, 49
Toxodera beieri, 126
Trametes versicolor, 116
Tree Bark Mantis, Danum Valley, 127
Trimeresurus borneensis, 179
Trithemis aurora, 4-5
Troides sp., 144
Tropical Swallowtail Moth, Danum Valley, 138-139
Tropidolaemus subannulatus, 178
Tropidophorus beccarii, 175
Tufted Ground Squirrel, Maliau Basin, 39
Turkey Tail Mushroom, Maliau Basin
Turtles and Tortoises, 184-185

U

Ultramafic rocks, Gunung Silam, 50, 51
UNDP, 21
Uropygids, Danum Valley, 153

V

Varanus rudicollis, 175
Violin Beetle, Danum Valley, 120
Viverra tangalunga, 39, 218-219

W

Wallace's Flying Frog, 2-3
Wallace's Flying Frog, Danum Valley, 30
Waterfalls, Imbak Canyon, 42
Waterfalls, Maliau Basin, 34
Western Tarsier, Danum Valley, 217
Whip Scorpions, Danum Valley, 153
White Grub Beetle, Danum Valley, 120
White-fronted Falconet, Danum Valley, 201
White-spotted Torrent Frog, Maliau Basin, 39
Worker Termites, Danum Valley, 146
Wreathed Hornbill, Danum Valley, 197

X

Xenochropis trianguligerus, 182

Y

Yayasan Sabah, Forest Management Area, 24, 34
Yellow-breasted Flowerpecker, Danum Valley, 100

Z

Zeuxidia amethystus amethystus, 140
Zulpha perlaria, 130